SOIL

Its Influence
on the History of the United States

PUBLISHED ON THE LOUIS STERN MEMORIAL FUND

Author of *The Paths of Inland Commerce* and Other Volumes

"Balds" in the Pumpkin Patch Mountains, North Carolina

SOIL

ITS INFLUENCE ON THE HISTORY OF THE UNITED STATES

WITH SPECIAL REFERENCE TO MIGRATION AND THE SCIENTIFIC STUDY OF LOCAL HISTORY

By Archer Butler Hulbert

Director of the Stewart Commission on Western History
of Colorado College

New Haven, Yale University Press
London, Humphrey Milford, Oxford University Press
1930

To

Philip Battell Stewart

and

Frances Cowles Stewart

friends of Yale, and founders of the Stewart Commission on Western
History, this volume is gratefully inscribed

PREFACE

THE *main theme of the present volume is the quite ignored one of the influences of the soil on American settlement and expansion. The plan of the volume, however, has been arranged in the hope of doing more than presenting merely a new and important phase of American history; it is offered as a kind of non-classroom text-book for those who may some day undertake to produce the constructive type of local histories so greatly needed. The material in its chapters has been elaborated from an outline delivered on the Goldwin Smith Lectureship Foundation at Cornell University, New York, in 1925.*

The introduction presents the dangers and pitfalls which surround one who deals with factors in history; the case of the geographer is cited as an example of how new and exceedingly valuable factors may be developed constructively—if poise and balance are maintained. Thus warning himself against the evil of being "possessed with the devil of one idea," the author presents in the succeeding five chapters illustrations of how geological, climatic, hydrographic, and edaphic factors have been and may be used to clarify history, particularly the history of American occupation and expansion.

There follow two chapters introducing the theme under the titles: "The Story of Our Soils" and "Soils and Migration." The thirteen succeeding chapters discuss the soil and correlated influences manifest in the founding of the chief pioneer American settlements on

the Atlantic seaboard and the expansion of population along the Pennsylvania–Valley of Virginia–Cumberland Gap route to the Mississippi Valley. The diversified economic opportunities offered in Kentucky lured there an eager and potentially important population; for beyond, in the rich Mississippi Basin, with St. Louis as its capital, was soon erected a new sociological Tower of Babel. A great dispersal of clans and races spread from this center—to Texas, Oregon, and California. We sum up in a chapter this far-famed dispersal, noticing particularly the edaphic influences which were always potent.

Nothing is more to be desired in the writing of American history than a new era of study of local history. The heyday of the old, ponderous county history, illuminated with photogravures of eminent citizens (the size being determined by the number of copies subscribed for) has quite passed away. Nothing better has taken its place; nothing worse could. In conclusion, therefore, the fruits of our study are presented to show how factors similar to those we have marshaled may be employed interestingly, and constructively, to develop the local history of any specific section or county in this country; how it is possible to assemble the geographic, climatic, and edaphic factors, conjointly with the economic and racial, as to make the story of any given distinct region alive, human, splendid.

A. B. H.

Colorado Springs,
   February, 1930.

CONTENTS

ILLUSTRATIONS

Introduction

AMERICAN HISTORY AND THE
NATURAL SCIENCES

THE proper interpretation of American history from the point of view of man in relation to natural environment is very desirable. But what is proper and what is not proper admits of much debate. In recent years the geographer has done a great deal to help us understand American history; the story of his development of this science, however, contains a lesson which we cannot learn too well.

The American Geographical and Statistical Society was formed in this country soon after the founding of the Royal Geographical Society of Great Britain, about the middle of the nineteenth century. The purpose of each of the societies was similar. Their object was the study of geography and its application to the development of commerce, to the distribution of animal and vegetable products, and to the human family. The first paper read before the American society was a memoir on "The Geography, History, Productions and Trade of Paraguay." The importance of such a study was recognized instantly, especially in its relation to commerce. The Society at once promised to become a clearing house too important to national economic development to retain any sort of a monopoly on this sort of investigation. Soon government agencies took up the work which these geographers had started and official bulletins and consular reports became the media of the kind of information which they had intended to circulate.

The first service of the geographer was, therefore, a notable one. About the beginning of the present century a new development of the science of geography was inaugurated. In American history Hume was to have the benefit of the researches of Mahaffy just as, for instance, Porter and McCosh in psychology were to benefit from the newer studies of James and Titchener.[1] Geologist and

[1] Such processes of development in other realms of study are common. In that of psychology, for instance, see A. E. Davies, "The Influence of Biology on the Development of Modern Psychology," *Psychological Review*, XXX, No. 3 (May, 1923), 164–175.

geographer combined to assist us very materially in understanding many factors in the making of our Republic which had hitherto been ignored. A pioneer work was done because a neglected field was at last covered. Intent upon their purpose, however, these geographical historians were at length accused of going too far, of confounding conditions with causes; the orthodox historians took up arms in a friendly way and protested against what they maintained was an injustice to history.

This reaction in academic circles was led, informally, by that winning and polite but no less caustic debater, Professor Burr of Cornell, who objected to having man canceled out of the historical equation. Constructive results were the outcome. A number of conferences to thrash the question out were arranged by the American Historical Association; one of these, presided over by Professor Turner in 1907, was of special clarifying value. Here Professor Burr and Professor George B. Adams laid down a line of reasoning of lasting significance. They pointed out that geography was but one factor in explaining history and that no more in history than in mathematics can the outcome be inferred by one factor alone. The new-school historian was, also, taken to task for a failure not at all uncommon to most of us—that of using ambiguous and inexact phraseology; as an example was cited the loose use of the word "location," in one case to describe an act and in another case to denote the result of an act. "To impute action or causation, influence or control," Professor Burr was quoted as saying, "to things which are inert is a figure of speech which gives vigor to style but which always involves a fallacy; and when to Nature is imputed what is planned and achieved by man, the sufferer from the fallacy is history." Most of the matters which the geographer calls upon us to include in history, said Professor Adams, are conditions, not causes. He warned all and sundry not to be deceived into thinking that it was the waterfall which ground the wheat.

Among the happy results which came from these discussions was the recognition of the very serious lack of cartographical material at the disposal of the average teacher; this led to the adoption of a plan on the part of the American Historical Association to prepare an adequate historical atlas, and in recent years numerous publishing firms, following this cue, have issued a large variety of atlases of more or less utility.

A second result of these conferences was more fundamental and far-reaching, and marked what we may call the third step in the service which the geographer-historian has rendered. No longer was he compelled to wage a battle for a recognition of the value of the factors which he considered essential. Important volumes now began to appear and a general recognition that a neglected factor in American history was being attended to marked the era; numerous monographs, notably those prepared under the auspices of the National Geographic Society (dating back as far as 1895), were published.

Hand in hand with this development came the equally important recognition that generalizations must be guarded against. Every scientist is, by nature, possessed with "the devil of one idea," as Professor Parks of Andover once said epigrammatically of the abolitionists. It is an admirable quality but it often works two ways. In the hand of a geographer or geologist who turns historian, or a historian who turns geographer, it may be dangerous, invaluable as the quality is of itself. The geologist who treats of the Hudson Valley as "the gateway to the continent" is likely, unless he weighs his words thoughtfully, to mislead many a novice. Geologically, the thesis is perfectly sound; historically one must remember that throughout the first important half century of early American migration from the Atlantic the Hudson-Mohawk route was the most effectually barred door to the interior of the continent. States across the Alleghenies had been admitted to the Union a decade before the Hudson "gateway" was really opened, and Lewis and Clark had gone to the Pacific before it began to resemble what it became—an enormously important avenue of expansion.

The lesson of the controversy indulged in by historians and geologists and geographers was evidently well learned. It was that great good comes from studying the relationships of these sciences and the interplay of their factors within narrow scopes, in specific cases and in particular localities. In the past generation a surprising number of special studies have been made by teachers and students, graduate and undergraduate, and others, as for instance Professor Sioussatt's study *Memphis as a Gateway to the West,* Professor Posey's *The Influence of Geographic Factors in the Development of Minnesota,* and Professor Surface's studies in Virginia history. True, only a beginning has been made; yet one may almost say that much of American history can well be rewritten by taking into account the factors of this character which have hitherto been very much neglected. The men who will assist in this work are appearing and they will succeed or fail in proportion as they maintain the balance necessary for their task. Causes and conditions must be adroitly diagnosed as such, and all factors must be given due consideration if the result is to approximate scientific accuracy.

The greatness of this task, however, is all too dimly seen even now. This is because in a myriad ways other sciences are interlinked with geography and should be given the consideration which is their due. To ignore any of these other handmaidens of history is as wrong as to ignore geographic and geologic factors. In fact so closely are botanic, edaphic, hydrographic, and climatic factors present in many problems which the geographer calls us insistently to recognize, that few have, or ever will, perhaps, differentiate carefully between them, or be aware when they shift from one to the other. Leading exponents of theories of the influence of climate, soil, and geography present interestingly confused discussions and jump nonchalantly from science to science. Despite the close correlation of these allied sciences, we should not cross boundary lines unwittingly or we shall fail to recognize the obligations which the facts impose.

Among the distinct services rendered by geology, one of history's most efficient handmaidens, has been the furnishing of physiographic maps. These maps are correct from the geologist's standpoint, yet in making history more understandable the historian might point out that a region having geologic solidarity, like the "Atlantic Plain," sometimes has little historic solidarity. The northern part of this plain is as different, historically, from the southern as the "Atlantic Plain" is different from the "Allegheny

Plateau" to the westward of it. No mapping of physiographic regions can have its proper meaning to students of history unless it takes into consideration the fact that different rocks have produced different soils; that different soils have produced different kinds of growths; that dissimilar soils under different climates have produced similar growths; and that soils which are alike produce different kinds of growths in different climates. The historian, so to speak, is interested in more superficial features of environment, soils, waterways, harbors, and lines of communications; the underlying strata of rock determined these in part, but a line must be drawn between geological and social physiographic regions.

This illustration brings frankly before us the inextricable mingling which automatically takes place when we begin to examine the relation of history to the natural sciences—every one of which, however, is pregnant with meaning for us. Almost insensibly we pass, in the case of geology, from a consideration of the framework of our continent to the soils formed by geologic processes, and then we catch the interesting picture of our land with its thousand-and-one types of soil, each bearing, or capable of bearing, its own quota of tree, shrub, plant, and grass. We see the long columns of the first immigrations to this land file by us, and note the reactions of these immigrants as they come from the Old World and locate in the New, adapt themselves to environments good, bad, or indifferent, or take up the bewildering and lawless filtering process of forming settlements along lines of natural selection, or, more often, of least resistance, all the way to the Pacific Ocean. Soils, climate, forest growths or the lack of these, plants, grasses—all to some degree or other had definite influences. Whether it was the Yankee moving westward, the Palatinate German planting the first granary of America in soils so like those of his native home, or the Scotch-Irish shunning the "dry" limestone soils which they looked upon with disfavor in Scotland, there is afforded for us interesting and enlightening speculation in the soil problem which geology has to offer us. Yet it is at once perceived how inextricably woven in this subject are questions of biology and especially botany. Soils may be inert. So was the cotton gin; but it gave millions of acres a new meaning to American history.

Climatology, also, is an important handmaiden to history. Our mountain ranges trend in a general way on northward and southward lines; as our national movement was to be from east to west these heights proved, of course, obstructions in the early day when transportation facilities were lacking. But the lines of climate and rainfall trend quite generally at right angles to these barriers, and they dictated the general zones of forest growth, grasses, etc. Our belts of hard woods and soft woods have a general east and west trend. In ways we have not been accustomed to note, these latter factors were of advantage to the European in his westward movement sufficient to aid him greatly in overcoming physical obstacles. Such influences of climate were subtle and easily led to misinterpretations. Yet they existed and must receive their proper recognition as factors.

Hydrography is one of history's handmaidens and will come to play an increasing part in making clearer some of the dim pages of our history. Linked closely with this science is that of aërography. In recent years attention has been paid to the study of sea-floor, ocean currents, tides, fogs, and wind currents as means of establishing facts hitherto not understood relative to explorations in our early history. An interesting illustration of how hydrography may make incidents in the far past plainer is found in looking at the St. Lawrence River and comparing it with the Mississippi from this standpoint. The current of the St. Lawrence flowed clear and sweet from a rocky upland; that of the Mississippi brought millions of tons of silt and mud down annually to block and metamorphose its many mouths. Up the St. Lawrence the ocean tides surge for more than a thousand miles; they force their way up the Mississippi only twelve. These enormously significant facts must be cited to aid in explaining why the St. Lawrence took a premier position as a key to the continent. They would have made that river the important pathway to the interior had there been no Great Lakes at its head.

It thus becomes plain, from this brief review, that history has numerous handmaidens, every one of which must come into range of the student's vision if we are to give a proper weight to all the factors which will aid us in arriving at correct solutions of historical problems and processes. Geography has been emphasized, and properly so; but it would be as great an error to ignore its correlated sciences, many of which have been loosely counted in as "geographical influences" when, scientifically, they were not properly geographical at all, as to ignore preëminent geographical factors.

But in the study of any factors provided by any science for a better understanding of history we must always stand ready to meet the challenge that historians made to the geographers: Conditions must not be confounded with causes and inexact phraseology will cost the user dear in loss of public confidence and esteem; generalities are to be avoided with rigor; and studies should trend toward the specific and intensive. Yet if these rules are honored, exploration in these fields should tend to produce much constructive work.

Chapter I

THE BASIS OF PROVINCES

THE necessity of understanding better the European background of American history has, in recent years, been seriously urged; as a result a more reasonable emphasis has been given to this essential phase of our history. Proper attention to these overseas origins of our Republic has aided many to recognize as never before that great events do not simply "happen." In focusing attention on the tree, the roots were neglected, with all the information they give as to the character of the growth which they make possible.

Our country is divided into various provinces; mark these out as you will—geographically, biologically, edaphically—they can never be genuinely understood unless attention be paid to their far-off origin. If we cannot understand American history without studying its European background, much less can we understand it without studying more attentively the American background of American history. It is one thing to understand, for instance, the geography of the Missouri River and its relationship to the iron region about Pittsburgh which made possible the quick transportation of materials to the edge of the Great Plains, rendering easier the conquest of those plains; but it brings a subtle sense of confidence, and a reliability of poise, to form a better acquaintance with the period when the Rockies rose and drove seaward that inland ocean which formerly connected the Arctic and Antarctic seas, and to catch the vision of the birth of those tiny rivulets which became mighty finger tips of the Mississippi. It makes all the difference between knowing a man and knowing both the man and his ancestry. If the student's background for the understanding of the rise and importance of Louisville at the strategic "Falls of the Ohio" is bounded by the accounts of Christopher Gist and Thomas Walker, and does not include the picture of the "Cincinnati uplift"—an island rising lonely and picturesque out of that giant inland sea—he misses a degree of confidence which might be his; and even in telling the story of La Salle's visit to "The Falls" far back in the seventeenth century, one is breaking into the middle of a mighty serial film without the assurance which comes from knowing the first sections of its story.

The background explanation of how New York state came to have her splendid passageway, unblocked by the Alleghenies, to the West by way of the Hudson-Mohawk valleys will be of interest so long as the Mohawk Trail, the Erie Canal, and the New York Central Lines are remembered. Gallant indeed was the struggle between New York, Philadelphia, and Baltimore to secure western trade by opening thoroughfares of commerce, roads, canals, and railways, to the trans-Allegheny country. But it cannot be seen perfectly by eyes which do not also see that other great battle fought in bygone ages when Nature filed down the northern tip of the Alleghenies in central New York, but left them standing, serried and hostile, in the rear of New York City's rivals, Philadelphia and Baltimore. Then the question was settled whether the Great Lakes were to find their outlet to the sea by way of the Mohawk or by way of the St. Lawrence. As the giant grip of the ice which covered this Northland was withdrawn, grooving the land as a modeler's hand molds the clay, this question of New York's triumph over her rivals was settled; in the place of mountain ranges blocking traffic here, we find, rather, the bed of the old geologic Lake Iroquois running east to west, now marked in part by the Mohawk River—giving to the region marked fertility of soil and an easy pathway of empire which became famous when the human obstacles, the aborigines, were removed. There is an important European background of New York state history in Holland; to neglect its study would be well-nigh fatal; and yet it would be equally unfortunate to slight its American background.

No factor is more important than this one relating to the origin and history of our rivers. Treatises on geographical influence commonly emphasize our heights of ground, our mountain ranges, particularly from the standpoint of their effect as obstacles to migration. The present writer's belief is that, as American history actually worked itself out, our mountain ranges exerted as many favorable as unfavorable influences; certainly migration nowhere ran low

merely because mountains were high, when gaps were present;
the great early population of the lower Ohio (now Kentucky)
gained that vantage point over the longest of routes and the highest of high-swung gateways, the Cumberland Gap. Rather would
the writer emphasize the need of study of our heights of ground
more from the standpoint of drainage; we should look upon our
rivers as living things and, as in the case of the Missouri mentioned above, see the romance of their birth, watch them grow up,
and take cognizance of the almost human subtlety exhibited by
some of them in their conflicts with rivals and with the obstacles
which lay in their path. The manner in which college men (to take
a class of citizens impervious to criticism) nonchalantly disregard
our rivers as they near their sources is nothing less than scandal-
ous; we need an impressionist map maker who would reverse the
conventional order and draw the lines of rivers broader and blacker
as their sources are reached, in order to bring out their tremendous
value as channels of continental migration and commerce.

This study of river valleys in terms of the highlands (which they
interpret in a practical fashion to students of history) may be
emphasized in two ways. One is by picturing America as the continent first showed above the waters, and seeing those first, cold
Archaean islands as they slowly grew larger, extending south and
southwest. Then came the birth of our first river—the vague Laurentian waterway along the general alignment of our present Great
Lakes. Thus it becomes plain that there could be no rivers until
land existed to be drained, and we are put in a position to recognize that rivers grew up along with a growing continent. A second
method of gaining this important viewpoint is to imagine one's self
making a journey, for instance, from the Atlantic Ocean to the
Mississippi River without crossing a natural stream of water. As
one heads the Kennebec, on such a cross-country run, he slips between the finger tips of that stream and those of the glittering
Chaudière on the north; swinging down around east of Lake
Champlain's feeders, he finds himself forging northward between
the Hudson River and Lake George; far up in New York state
the tributaries of the Hudson are skirted, and he is driven southward by the network of streams focusing on the "Finger Lake"

region and the Oswego Valley. At Rome, New York, he finds the
strategic key between the Mohawk and the western streams and
lakes. From there the journey is less subject to pitfalls, and, by
way of such important spots as Akron, Ohio, Fort Wayne, Indiana,
South Bend, Indiana, Chicago's outskirts, and Portage, Wisconsin,
the journey is completed to the Mississippi—and a new concept
of our waterways in relation to our highlands is obtained. Other
reflections, to be mentioned in their place, are forced upon one in
contemplating this imagined experience.

With these practical illustrations of the value of getting the far
background in view, we come back to the main question. Our
provinces—in whatever terms we draw them—came into existence
as naturally as did our rivers. Wherever we look, the world had
one universal foundation, the layer of rock known as the Archaean,
which was deposited in the first period of "time." What we call
time is reckoned by what has been superimposed upon this stone
foundation on which the world structure has been erected.

First, a series of Archaean islands stood above the waters of
the sea, resembling in composition the main constituent of salt
water. These islands marked what we now know as the Laurentian
and Huronian highlands of northern Michigan, Wisconsin, New
York, and Ontario, where, in many cases, the rock lies as bare to
the sun and stars as it did in that era millions of years ago when
"America" was a mere rocky archipelago. Other islands dotted the
Atlantic coast from Nova Scotia to the highlands of New Jersey;
the Blue Ridge was represented by a few islands; while far away
across a western sea lonely islands marked the present Wind River
and Laramie ranges of the Rocky Mountains. Few as these islands
were, they defined the continental plan; "the evolution of the
grand structural plan of the continent was, hence, early commenced," says Dana, "and the system thus initiated was the system to the end." The contemplation of the idea that our continent
was built according to specification is an impressive one; through
countless years the framework has been forming and the process
is going on today as rapidly as ever.

This concept of a living, growing continent is valuable, even if
the exact formula may always be a debated question. The develop-

ment of the Archaean islands was toward the south and south-west. In the Paleozoic period land masses extended first to central New York and, in the Age of Fishes (Devonian), it reached the southern extremity of that state, while from the original land masses in the Lake Superior region the growth extended into central Minnesota, Illinois, and Iowa.

The giant inland sea to the southwest was severed by the rise of the "Cincinnati uplift," heretofore mentioned, although for ages the plan of the Mississippi Basin and the western half of our continent was only indicated by the thin line of islands which first marked the course of the Rockies; in the carboniferous period in the East land masses crept down into the Carolinas.

The magnificent stage was now set for the development of our American West in the Mesozoic age when the Sierra Nevada revolution was followed by the rise of the Rocky Mountains. Through this and the Cenozoic age the battle royal was fought out between the land and the inland sea; slowly it was driven back as the "Gulf of Mexico" receded doggedly from what is now the junction of the Ohio and Mississippi to its present confines, while in the East the present seacoast from the "Fall Line" to our existing coast line was lifted from the Atlantic and mountains of Alpine grandeur were piled up across what is now New England.

When it seemed the great task was completed, there came that monstrosity of earthly phenomena—the advance of successive ice caps out of the North, moving southward to a line roughly represented by Mason and Dixon's line, the Ohio and Missouri rivers. These freakish afterthoughts of creation had their notable effects in establishing the drainage systems mentioned previously; other effects of these phenomena will be treated elsewhere.

Thus were created our physiographic regions,[1] at different times —some in very ancient days, some in the last phases of this great drama—in different ways, through volcanic action, through molding by the ice cap, through risings and subsidences of seas and sea-

[1] Atlantic plains, Piedmont plateaus, Appalachian ranges, Allegheny plateaus, New England plateaus, lake plains, prairie plains, Ozark plains, the Great Plains (plateaus), the Stony mountains, Park mountains, Columbia plateaus, Colorado plateaus, basin ranges, and Pacific plains and plateaus.

floors, and through erosion. They are of all ages, types, sizes, and shapes; they are of all formations and mixtures of formations, geologically; of all soils, in many cases, and of all mixtures of soils. For the most part they represent drainage areas, although sometimes several are found in one drainage area.

Theoretically the basis of provinces is geological and topographical. Practically, from the historians' standpoint, the basis of provinces was their soils and growths and their economic and political influences. The underlying rock foundations forever have their significance, little as this was recognized when the process of filling the continent with its early population was going on. But superficial "controls" exerted by climate, precipitation, soils, forests, meadow lands, and drainage systems, dominated.

The artificial boundaries, based on geology, must be recognized; they are particularly valuable in indicating drainage areas so far as they do. Practically, one such province may be found to contain a number of provinces when the influence of these superficial controls on man is considered. In general, biology not geology, is of prime assistance in aiding us to study the real provinces which arose—provinces which produced wheat here and corn there, cotton here and tobacco there, Aroostook potatoes here, and butter and cream there. With this basis of provinces these chapters will specifically deal.[2]

[2] Professor F. J. Turner, alone among our students, has seen through to the deeper meaning of "province" and "section"; and those who have not read and reread his "Geographical Influences in American Political History" (*Bulletin of the American Geographical Society*, XLVI, No. 8 [August, 1914], 591–595) may well do so. These pregnant sentences are to the point for us:

Sections are more important than States in shaping the underlying forces of American history. . . . The country itself is too large an area to tell the whole. It often lies athwart diverse geographical areas, and has diverse economic and social groups within it. . . . Mapping by election precincts . . . would be a much more satisfactory mode of exhibiting the relations of voting to soils, resources, position, population, etc. . . . The facts demand combined investigation by geographer and historian.

Cf. the same author's "Section and Nation," *The Yale Review*, XII (October, 1922), I.

Chapter II

CLIMATIC INFLUENCES ON MAN
AND VEGETATION

MANY of the influences of climate, its relation to and also apart from geography, have been analyzed by numerous physical geographers and others. Professor Huntington of Yale has made signal contributions to this subject; and yet we have very far to go in learning the subtle ramifications of these forces acting on man's environment, character, migrations, and creative and selective processes. Those who favor the theory that these factors are too subtle to be handled constructively have good grounds for their opinion. Nowhere have generalizations been more loosely made than here; nowhere has the boundary line between correlated sciences been more nonchalantly crossed by investigators without scruple and without passport. Yet the influences of climate on man have been marked; it is the theory of the present writer, however, that they are to be constructively studied by confining attention rather closely to the effects on vegetation and on man. If the scientist, possessed by his "devil of one idea," brings a good deal of evidence into court which must be thrown out as immaterial, our attitude should be of the balanced type which recognizes the worth of the enthusiasm even if much of the product of the enthusiasm seems worthless. That Professor Huntington's data are limited is a matter of greater regret to him than to his critics; such facts and laws as those for which he has searched are exceedingly difficult to attain; we should be grateful for the wheat he has produced—not petulant because of the amount of chaff.[1]

[1] Studies of this character are seldom more interesting than when they tend to disprove theories formerly honored. An illustration of this is the work done in Europe by Pittard, Karmin, and Kappeyne on the relationship of the height of human bodies to climate, soil, and rock strata. Of the findings Dr. Lalog writes:

It is very hard to determine the respective importance of the many factors that play a part in determining the height of the human body. Race evidently is the most important; social environment also has an undeniable influence. Is physical environment also influential? This has sometimes been asserted without positive proof. To solve the problem Messrs. Pittard, Karmin, and

The general influences of climate directly on man are almost too patent to be discussed. Peoples in colder climates require and display more energy than those of warm latitudes; it is estimated that in winter the energy requirement is greater by eight hundred calories than in summer. The climate of New England had marked influence in all our early history before modern conveniences for combating cold weather were known. The preparation of the wise Yankee farmer against the event of being "snowbound," the plan of closely grouped living which was necessary to meet harsh conditions, the necessity of a people's being tightly housed four or five months out of every year—all naturally influenced life and character.

These effects can be measured so whimsically and from such varied points of view, and the whole be so distorted, that it is doubtful if they should be more than mentioned in passing. Climate everywhere dictated, to a degree, architectural types of buildings, and to some extent these followed isothermal lines; yet predilections brought from foreign homelands had, doubtless, a stronger influence than climate. Trades and occupations which were carried on mainly out of doors, where raw materials were available, were likely to have more development where winters were mild than where they were severe. The endless New England house, running from the "parlor" to the outermost confines of the hennery and pigsty, grew up naturally with the long New England winters.

Kappeyne have undertaken a series of investigations on height in the Swiss cantons. These territories, of small extent and of rather homogeneous population, are well fitted for a study of this sort, because of the variety of their physical conditions. The first of these studies is devoted to Valais and . . . is based on figures from the military recruitment for 1889–91. Race, habitation, and food are very uniform in this canton, and its very simple arrangement of mountain and valley makes possible some interesting comparisons.

The results of this study show, we are told, that bodily height varies with altitude, having a tendency to be greater at higher places—which is precisely contrary to the theory of ancient writers. The influence of sunlight and of the underlying geological strata is also investigated. That of the former is very easily studied in Valais, since the canton is split in two by the Rhone Valley, of which the right slope faces the south and the left slope the north. Dr. Lalog continues:

Comparing zones of equal altitude, it is found that places on the left bank have taller inhabitants than those on the right bank, altho the latter receives more sunlight. This is true in three out of four zones of altitude and in eleven out of thirteen districts. . . . For all three kinds of factors studied, the results are in contradiction to hitherto received hypotheses. In Valais, height does not decrease as altitude increases; it is greater in regions less exposed to the sun and also greater on primitive rock than on limestone (*Journal de Statistique Suisse* quoted in *Cosmos*, December 14, 1907).

There, too, the fact that buildings had to be provided for the safe housing of cattle in severe weather had the effect of limiting the numbers of herds to what necessity required; at the same time the paucity of needed fodder doubtless had a great effect.

Social customs and education were doubtless influenced by climate, although no constructive discussion of this subject is possible. When someone outdoes Professor Huntington by showing from the books of ancient optical specialists that more eyesight was ruined to the square acre in New England than to the square mile farther south, then we shall have proof either that more reading was indulged in in New England than elsewhere or that Yankee spectacle makers were less efficient than their southern rivals—which? Doubtless a housed-up people come to be given more to reading and study than an out-of-doors people. And it is very probable that a flourishing of organizations such as churches and lyceums, which depend upon the gathering of people into congregations and audiences, will be seen to a marked degree where a harsh climate exerts its centripetal influence; the centrifugal influence of the automobile is much commented on today by all social organizers. Whether climate, however, gives the New Englander a more solid basis for his boast that his section has dominated the nation educationally, would be much disputed; in a specific crisis, such as the Constitutional Convention of 1787, where information and education were, so to speak, at an epoch-making premium, the South stands ready for any comparison the student desires to make on the basis of the intellectual efficiency of its representation.

The foregoing argument fully establishes our contention that much of the discussion relative to climatic influences is not constructive. The rule laid down with reference to all discussion of geographic problems applies here pointedly; only the intensive study of very specific matters is worth while. These are to be found, and the relation of climate to transportation is one of them. The position of Cairo, Illinois, as the most northerly ice-free port on the Mississippi River, exerted a dominating influence on the early railway-building program of the state of Illinois. This was a factor in the old-time control which more southerly Atlantic

Ocean ports, such as Baltimore and Charleston, exerted on our seaboard. It was a strong argument used in favor of westward-reaching canals in Pennsylvania and Maryland, because the milder winters there gave a promise that these canals would not be so blocked with ice as the rival Erie Canal to the northward, and would therefore be kept open more months in the year.

In a different way, on the other hand, the climatic argument was employed in ways favorable to the most northerly Erie Canal. As Ohio and her sister states began to raise greater and still greater crops of wheat early in the nineteenth century, the dangers encountered in sending the abundant surplus of grain down the only route available to market—the Ohio and Mississippi rivers—became formidable. The uncertainty of this method of transportation, the long delays at such spots as the "Falls of the Ohio" at Louisville while awaiting a rise in the river, became serious handicaps. Wheat in ships' holds soured in the semitropic zone to which those river channels led, even when delays were avoided. The final argument which influenced the deciding vote in the Ohio Legislature, for instance, in favor of building a thousand miles of northward-leading canals in that state was the argument of the wheat grower that his crop could go to market by way of the Great Lakes and the Erie Canal under climatic conditions most auspicious for its preservation and sale.

The range taken by students of climatic influence is wide; in their discussions climate will be found to have been a factor in religious, governmental, political, and economic development. Any survey of this growing mass of material will convince the investigator that a modicum of truth permeates the whole and that, where balance has been maintained, constructive results have been achieved. The relation of droughts to advances and retardations of populations, the compensations found in wells and subsoil water in our western states, the development of the system of irrigation and dry farming, the more complete examination of the relationship of the zones occupied by fur-bearing animals and of the organization of associations to secure furs to the later movement of population into the selfsame regions—all are subjects which the climatologist has studied and may further investigate with profit to the historian.

The constant invasion of the climatologist into the realms of biology and plant life for data of supposedly climatic character leads us to recognize that we must look to the biologist for the most reliable data for study of climatic influences on national development. And while we will find the three sciences represented by climate, plant life, and soils indissolubly united, the most striking expression of these factors will be usually found in plant life.

Seldom, it is true, is it given to a biologist to put a much disputed historical problem into his test tube or under his microscope and give us a correct solution at which the historian would perhaps never otherwise have arrived. That this has been done once has its very far-reaching suggestion and opens more doors of useful investigation in early American history than a superficial glance will suggest. The biologist concerned was Professor Fernald of the Gray Herbarium, who, becoming interested in the discussion as to where the Norsemen planted their colony of "Wineland the Good" along the coast of our continent, undertook to solve it by tracing back to Iceland words which were used in the Sagas to describe the fruit, plants, and trees that the Norsemen found on our coast.

He found that the word *vinber* meant mountain cranberries, not "grapes," as it had usually been translated; that *hveiti* meant strand wheat, not "Indian corn," and that *mosurr* meant canoe birch, not "maple."[2] Thus was the ancient contempt of George Bancroft for "Norse fakes" and James P. Dexter's patient groping for the truth in his entomological laboratory, made honorable by a biologist who located "Wineland the Good" between Labrador and the Gulf of St. Lawrence where floristic conditions answer the premises named by the ancient sagas.

This case stands by itself, and we may seldom see it equaled, but it carries many suggestions especially to all who are interested in the history of the occupation of this continent by Europeans

[2] M. L. Fernald, "Notes on the Plants of Wineland the Good," *Rhodora*, XII (February, 1910), 17–38.

and the westward progress of pioneers into its vast interior.[3] Proper attention has not been paid to the *vinber, hveiti,* and *mosurr* factors in American expansion. In a day when most men—practically all the expansionists—were agriculturists, such factors exerted a control greater than all others. The seminar student who, becoming interested in problems of this character, asserted that one ought to be able to tell whether a man on an Indiana farm was a Republican or Democrat from the soil of his farm and its growths, was taking on quite a contract; but he was getting hold of a series of influences of geology and botany of great value to those who wish to evaluate some factors that must not be ignored in the future as they have been in the past. We may be very far from being able to distinguish Democrats, Republicans, Presbyterians, Congregationalists, Scotch-Irish, Cavaliers, Mennonites, and Holy Rollers by the soils on which they live and the products of those soils; but the fact remains that in the formative period of our history several "provincial" areas were occupied by these various classes of people, and that many of the affinities and prejudices, likes and dislikes created by soil-and-plant factors projected themselves into later history as men began to move out from their eastern hives or breeding zones to the westward.

Professor Warming of Copenhagen, in developing his researches in plant migration has offered, consciously or not, to the student of history the basis for a profitable analogy between plant and human migration. Those who tend to lay down strict laws for the latter may well consider the fantastic assortment of devices adopted by Nature to scatter her children over the earth, as illustrated by the ragweed and tumbleweed and thistle, by the membranous wings of maple and elm seed, the attractive power of bright seeds and flowers to lure to them the winged vehicles which will spread abroad their pollen or seed. Not less innumerable among men were the methods and means and reasons for migration. The canniness with which plants, when overcrowded, get rid

[3] A new approximation of the date of pueblo building in the Southwest by studying tree rings in timbers used is a new contribution of biology to history. See A. E. Douglass, "The Secret of the Southwest Solved . . . ," *National Geographic Magazine,* LVI, No. 6 (December, 1929), 737–770.

of the weaker members, is not unlike the process to be observed in the human species. The development of ability on the part of plants to defend themselves, seemingly, by growing in thickets (as canebrake, blackberries) and so avoiding the attacks of enemies, may be likened to the "compact-making" Yankee as he moved out into the wilderness by forming groups for mutual protection; and, just as the acacia puts out juice on the end of its leaves which attracts colonies of ants that keep off injurious parasites, so the wise Quakers offered rich lands on their borders free to the doughty Irish and Scotch-Irish who would keep off the red-skinned foes from their colony.

Existing kinds of plants owe their structure and habits to a very considerable degree "to the operation of the struggle for existence; . . . this term including [to quote Professor Bergen] the effort to respond to the changes in the conditions by which they are surrounded." A parallelism here is not out of place when drawn between the weed which endures trampling upon and still lives, which makes a successful fight for life on any soil, which endures every manner of exposure to cold and frost, and yet succeeds in self-pollenization, produces seeds, and disperses them, with what some have considered the "weeds" of civilization—that uncouth throng of the vanguard of pioneers which flung itself with such lustiness upon a wild American frontier, endured indescribable vicissitudes, and developed into a flowering of which all the world became proud. In this process feral arts which were adopted have been frequently mentioned. But, too, the art of plant, tree, and bush to maintain existence was also adopted. The dead nettle mimics the appearance of a poisonous plant (the stinging nettle); plants take on the likeness of pebbles or earth and so avoid destruction; here wood forms too hard to be of use, as in the case of hardhack or ironweed, and there plants arm themselves with bristles, thorns, or hairs, as in the case of the barberry and nightshade. On the other hand we find plants accumulating unpleasant or poisonous odors as if to provide themselves with weapons against enemies, as in the case of the dog fennel, hound's-tongue, tomato plant, buckeye, tansy, etc. Who shall say that these arts of defense, so comparable to human defenses, were not developed by ancient environment for the very purposes which they actually served so well?

The American pioneer, in turn, also owed his structure and habits to a considerable degree to the operation of the struggle for existence, this term also including the effort to respond "to the changes in the conditions by which he was surrounded." He was here an acacia, there a stinging nettle or barberry, and somewhere else a hound's-tongue or a tansy.

Like the migrating plant the migrating pioneer followed a line of natural selection dominated by the soil-and-climate factor. Some day a successor to Warming or to Fernald will bring out clearly this analogy between plant and human migration. He will draw a true comparison between the American migration and the story of the battles and battle grounds, the geographical, topographical, climatic, and edaphic factors of plant migration. He will take perhaps as his illustration, the epic story of how vegetation replanted the region all but desolated by the ice sheets which covered the northern part of the United States. He will show how, as the last ice sheet retreated, this epoch-making conquest was led by the William Pynchons and Daniel Boones of plant life—the tundra, mat-herbage, and other hardy growths now found only in polar regions. It was fortunate that mountains high enough (such as Roan Mountain) existed in the southern Alleghenies to provide by their altitude a habitat suitable to these and other plants. From these reservoirs—not unlike the reservoirs provided on the Atlantic coasts for the temporary preservation of human stock which came from Europe—regiment on regiment of floristic stocks marched back northward to their despoiled homeland. The process was merely a falling back of refugee species into the zonal relations to which long environment had adjusted them.

In some such way—and the likeness is worth attention—from their early zones of occupation on our seaboard or from their transatlantic homes, the Yankee and Virginian, Palatinate German, Scotch-Irish, Irish, and Huguenot, led the way into our western expanses; these, too, had acquired zonal relations which long environment had taught them to crave. And as, in the case of the northward march of the floristic species which had been hibernating in the southern Alleghenies, the sweet gum and persimmon went no farther north than the lower Hudson, just so the Palatinate Germans went at first, no farther than the limestone lands of Penn's empire which were so like their Rhine Valley homeland in their wheat-bearing qualities, or to the famous Orangeburg soils of like character in the Carolinas farther south. And just as the oak, hickory, and chestnut pushed on beyond the sweet gum and persimmon to the Great Lakes Basin farther north, so did the Scotch-Irish push on beyond the limestone soils which they had learned to fear in their Old World homeland to the slate and shale region behind—a land somewhat similar to that from which the stock originated beyond the seas.

Thus in the world of plant life we find a biological phase of the "patriotism" which, as Partridge in his *Psychology of Nations* has shown, develops in man—the devotion to a physical country as home; as certain kinds of soils and climates influenced these refugees flocking back to their despoiled homeland, so certain kinds of trees, soils, crops, topography, and streams exerted a subtle control over our early migrations. The passionate desire of the southern mountaineer who has gone down to work in southern factories to get back into the mountains, and his belief that one draught of water from the old spring will give him back his health, is an echo of this patriotism; so, also, is the hidden refrain (the "movies" to the contrary notwithstanding), of Lomax' cowboy songs—the desire not to be buried on the "lone prairies" and the warning to other boys not to leave their old homes in the East.

We now see in the possible analogy which the trained scientist will some day make for us the real meaning of the fact that our lines of precipitation, temperature, etc., which dictated all wild and cultivated growths, ran along approximately east and west lines. Yet in how marked a way did human plants follow these is shown in the fact that, where these lines do not very well approximate true east and west lines, migration also varied, and much in the same direction as the lines of precipitation and temperature. Elsewhere we shall see this in a clearer light as specific application to definite areas is made. It is believed that the most satisfactory method of ascertaining definite influences of climate on man is to hold steadfast to the proven influences which climate has had on vegetation and determine its influences in turn on migrations and settlements. That these can be examined with a reasonable degree of scientific exactness, it will be our purpose to show.

Chapter III

THE WATERWAY KEYS TO OUR
SOIL PROVINCES

THE sciences of aërography and hydrography are comparatively new and we probably have only an incomplete idea even of the promise which they hold out as interpreters of our history. Something has been done, however, to suggest that as biology has materially aided us in solving some problems, so these sciences may also make contributions which will clarify our understanding of several hidden passages in the story of American discovery, exploration, and occupation.

It is now an accepted fact that there has been little if any change since the coming of the first Europeans to our shores in the direction and intensity of ocean currents off our coasts and in the estuaries of our American rivers. Infinitesimal influences have probably been exerted by some of the works of man's hand along our coasts, but these do not go further, perhaps, than very slightly to alter the temperature of the water through canal-making within certain very restricted areas. Tides and currents run, fogs rise and drift, practically as they did in the day when Columbus, Drake, and Hawkins sailed the ocean, and produce today the same results. The continuous effects of these molding elements have, of course, steadily modified our coast lines, save as here and there man has erected protective barriers. Yet, with reference to the sea floor, while changes have taken place, it is probable that we do not go far wrong in assuming that compensating factors have so operated that we can count upon the assumption that in 1492 it was very much what it is today.

On the other hand aërographers now assure our airplane experimenters that our notion of winds as the most fickle of natural phenomena is scientifically at fault. The regularity of certain winds was understood in the earliest periods of history, but to be told that most of our main air currents are quite reliable is comparatively new; and to be told that we are correct in thinking that these currents ran in the olden day of American exploration just about as they do today, gives a basis for reëxamination of the era of exploration in the light of facts now being brought to light as the science of aërography takes a new place.

The combination thus effected by new developments in the sciences of hydrography and aërography assist the unraveling of many of the seeming eccentricities and vagaries of early American exploration. They also tend to give us new ideas of the meaning and influence of the American rivers which acted as waterway keys to our soil provinces, as the illustration given by a comparison of the Mississippi and St. Lawrence rivers has already suggested. From this new vantage point also, as by "averted vision," we ought to come to look upon our American rivers opening into the Atlantic Ocean from a new perspective, especially as the factors of climate, soil, and vegetation previously treated are taken into consideration in connection with aërography and hydrography.

Fortunately we have at hand the record of a definite piece of critical study made by scientists, in the sphere of historical clarification, which stands out as signally in its way as the valuable bit of illumination cast by Professor Fernald on the problem of "Wineland the Good." Reference is made to the study made by the late Professor George Davidson on our Pacific coast in connection with his work for the United States Coast and Geodetic Survey.[1] In summarizing his findings Professor Davidson says:

With the present knowledge of our coast it is possible to locate Ulloa; to track Cabrillo and Ferrelo in their discoveries in mid-winter; to place Drake under Cape Ferrelo and Point Reyes, and to fix with certainty the most of Vizcaino's positions. . . . I have endeavored to put myself in their places; and understanding the seasons and the difficulties they encountered, I have tried to follow them day by day in their exciting discoveries. . . . I have reduced the Coast Survey chart of the vicinity of Drake's Bay to correspond in scale and orientation, whereby I have identified his bay.[2]

[1] U.S. Coast and Geodetic Report, 1886, Appendix 7.
[2] House Executive Documents, Second Session, Nineteenth Congress, pp. 155–156.

In parallel columns Professor Davidson sketches the routes of these explorers, with comments of his own on the variations of their compass readings and with identifications of the points of land mentioned in the original explorers' logs. It is said that the early navigators were often wrong in locating their position at sea. While their estimates of longitude were largely guesswork, it is interesting to have such proof as Professor Davidson furnishes that those of latitude were sometimes exactly correct, as in the case of Drake's placing Drake's Bay at 38°.

Professor Davidson's fine scientific spirit, as illustrated by his unwillingness to be handicapped by the vagueness of the translations of the journals of the old-time explorers and so making better ones for his own use, is a suggestion to any student led to try to prove a historical problem in the aërographic-hydrographic test tube.

Director Alexander McAdie of the Blue Hill Observatory has profited by the example of his famous preceptor and has carried on, as time permitted, investigations suggested by Davidson's studies. In his valuable paper entitled "Nova Albion, 1579" we are presented with the data of an aërographer directed toward the exploitation of a topic similar to that treated by Professor Davidson.[3] This treatment of like topics by men preëminently interested in different sciences is valuable. McAdie had long been a student of the California coast, its currents, tides, and fogs.[4] Upon the historical problem of the range of Drake's famous voyage in the *Golden Hind* this aërographer brings to bear a new set of factors which tend to substantiate the decisions reached by his teacher; however, we are more interested in the processes than in any specific finding. He says:

. . . weather was responsible both directly and indirectly for many of the episodes of Drake's voyage. Certainly it played an important part in determining the courses. . . . If we can prove the constancy of certain climatic factors, we may use these to great advantage in interpreting the narrative of the voyage. Indeed they become extremely valuable in identifying the courses and the various anchorages.[5]

---

[3] *American Antiquarian Society Proceedings,* 1918.
[4] "The Rainfall of California," *University of California Publications,* 1913.
[5] "Nova Albion, 1579," p. 4.

As to the reliability of these factors and the scientific accuracy of judging past by present wind systems, McAdie cites the testimony of Dr. Bauer, who was in charge of the magnetic work of the Carnegie Institution and who compares the route taken by Edmund Halley's ship, the *Paramour Pink*, of 1700 with that of a nonmagnetic ship operated by the Institution as follows:

Two sailing ships cruising in the Atlantic Ocean from port to port, the one in 1700 and the other in 1910, were forced by the prevailing winds to follow very closely identical courses. If, however, these two vessels had been directed to follow certain definite magnetic courses, and if we may suppose that they had such motive power as to render them independent of the winds, then their respective paths would have diverged considerably. . . . In brief while the sailing directions as governed by the winds over the Atlantic are the same now as they were during Halley's time the magnetic directions or bearings of the compass that a vessel must follow to reach a given port have greatly altered.[6]

Applying the test of wind currents McAdie checks up and is in agreement with Davidson's findings based on hydrography and they settle beyond hope of contradiction the point that Drake could not have gone north to 48° nor given England a claim either to Oregon or Washington beyond 43° north latitude.[7] That it was at Point Reyes, not farther north or south, where Drake stopped and cleaned the foul bottom of his famous ship, naming the country "Nova Albion," is well established by weather factors presented by McAdie. Whether or not Drake "picked up" San Francisco Bay cannot be proven, but that the sojourn was at Point Reyes, and not in that Bay, is proven by the fact that such weather as Drake encountered is never known in the Bay in the month of July. So befogged was the doughty captain of the *Golden Hind* that he records "neither could we at any time in the whole fourteen days together find the aire so clear to be able to take the height of sunne or starre." In fact Davidson at Point

[6] Quoted from the fourth Halley Lecture delivered at Oxford, May 22, 1913 (*ibid.*, p. 5).

[7] "Francis Drake on the Northwest Coast of America," *Trans. Geographic Society of the Pacific*, V (Series 2), 1908. The last edition of the *Encyclopedia Britannica* perpetuates the error that Drake made 48°.

Reyes, in 1859, reported continuous fog for thirty-nine days, and McAdie found that in a five-year record for 185 days ninety-seven were days of fog. Whole days of fog in San Francisco Bay in July are unknown, or so rare they may be said to be unknown.

These studies in aërography, hydrography, and climate point out the way for more investigation. They summon us, for instance, to seek from specialists in these fields a new meaning, historically, in the courses of the Gulf Stream and other ocean currents which determined, more than they have been given credit for, the alignment of early American exploration. Cartier's floundering about off the mouth of the Gulf of the St. Lawrence becomes very plain when the tides and currents of that section are plotted in connection with his ship's track; they explain the turning back of the *Mayflower* from her original objective which was not Cape Cod; and looking forward to the day when the heavens may be filled with "argosies of magic sails," it is probable that as topography has been a factor of importance in determining strategic centers of terrestrial activity, the air currents now first faintly plotted by our Cartiers and Drakes of the air, are likely to be important factors in redetermining, in a measure, centers of future activity.

But, of greater importance to our present study than any special application of the subject mentioned, is the view gained from its vantage point—the relationship of the Atlantic to our coasts and their key-waterways which offered access to fertile land. Rivers are the keys to all continents. The conquests, military or social, of valleys like those of the Rhine, Seine, Euphrates, St. Lawrence, Mississippi, and Columbia have been in considerable part the history of the world. The explorers who have found our great streams have played a momentous rôle in human affairs.[8] A glance at the

[8] The following is a list of navigable rivers of the Atlantic coast together with their available depths:

River	State	Least Water Feet	Mean H.W. Feet	Navigable to
St. Croix	Maine	17	37	The Ledge
Machias	Maine	19½	32½	Machiasport
Penobscot P.	Maine	14	27	Bangor
St. George	Maine	16	25¼	Thomaston
Damariscotta	Maine	9	17½	Damariscotta and Newcastle

River	State	Least Water Feet	Mean H.W. Feet	Navigable to
Sheepscot	Maine	30	39¾	Wiscasset
Kennebec	Maine	24	30	Bath
Kennebec	Maine	11	15	Augusta
Saco	Maine	7	16	Biddeford and Saco
Piscataqua	N. H.	75		Portsmouth
Merrimac	Mass.	9	17	Newburyport
Charles	Mass.	16	25	Boston
Chelsea	Mass.	18	27	Boston
Taunton	Mass.	7½	11	Taunton
Providence	R. I.	25	29½	Providence
Providence	R. I.	15	21	Pawtucket
Thames	Conn.	26	28½	New London
Thames	Conn.	13	16	Norwich
Connecticut	Conn.	12	13	Hartford
Hudson	N. Y.	40	44	New York
Hudson	N. Y.	24	28	Hudson
Hudson	N. Y.	12	15	Troy
Delaware	N. J.	30	35	Philadelphia
Delaware	N. J.	10	14½	Trenton
Chester	Md.	11	13	Chestertown
Choptank	Md.	12	13¾	Cambridge
Patapsco	Md.	35	36	Baltimore
Susquehanna	Md.	12	14	Havre de Grace
Potomac	Md.	22	25	Washington
Patuxent	Md.	23	24½	Benedict
Severn	Md.	30	31	Annapolis
Elk	Md.	10½	12	Chesapeake City
Rappahannock	Va.	14	16	Rappahannock
York	Va.	20	23	West Point
James	Va.	35	37½	Newport News
James	Va.	18	21½	Richmond
Elizabeth	Va.	35	37½	Norfolk and Portsmouth
Cape Fear	N. C.	26	30½	Wilmington
Ashley	S. C.	28	33¼	Charleston
Beaufort	S. C.	18	25	Port Royal
Savannah	Ga.	24	30½	Savannah
Brunswick	Ga.	22	29	Brunswick
St. John's R.	Fla.	21	24	Jacksonville
St. Marys	Fla.	16	22	St. Marys
GULF COAST				
Mobile	Ala.	23	24½	Mobile
Mobile	Ala.	14		45 miles— headwater
Mississippi	La.	31	32½	New Orleans
Brazos	Tex.	13½	15¼	Surfside

appended table of American Atlantic coast streams brings out the fact that length of navigability is only one factor, and often a small one, in the matter of a river's control of colonization. The kinds of soil in the valleys to which these waterways led was the prime concern until manufacturing with water power became common.

The relation of our waterways to our provincial regions has not been studied attentively. There is a distinct value in approaching the question of provinces from this standpoint. It must be evident that the blueprints of provinces, as we have had them presented to us heretofore, are laid out quite independently of our rivers; and yet it was in general along these river pathways that migration entered our country, and it was in river valleys of approximately similar character of climate and soil that the real provincial kingdoms were established. These soil-series which, as will be shown later, dominated early American expansion, run across river drainages as frequently as with them. Almost everywhere in the Mississippi Valley the soil-series cross the valley at right angles. This is an important point to hold in view if, as is so greatly needed, we are to get a more lifelike impression of our geography as a factor in the nation-building process. A river may be a key—to a drainage system or a province; but unless we see that a river may have unlocked several provinces, physiographic or edaphic, we miss a valuable part of the vision. The proper view of the Ohio River for example, is possible only as we see that it was a link between regions producing coal and those producing wheat, and a link between other regions producing pork and tobacco, cotton and whiskey, corn and lead. An appreciation of how many "doors" our rivers unlocked is greatly worth while.

Chronologically, however, the first mission of our rivers was that of being heralds of the continent. So long as men were of the opinion that Columbus had discovered only an archipelago, so long was actual discovery of the continent delayed. Soon, however, the telltale evidence furnished by the giant Orinoco crystallized opinion as to a continental mass in that southern region; no mere island stream could throw fresh water so far into the sea that it could be dipped up out of sight of land as did that river.

Yet oddly enough, the declaration made by the Orinoco led to an inference wholly wrong. The Mississippi and St. Lawrence held tightly to their great secret; the gulfs and islands at their mouths allowed no current to push out into the sea. Men therefore inferred that a continent lay to the southward and a mass of islands to the northward, and for a century rivaled each other in finding the "northwest" passageway through the latter to the Indies and Cathay. This point should be held steadily in mind; what happened is not otherwise understood. At first neither the St. Lawrence, Penobscot, Kennebec, or Hudson rivers stood for anything except possible keys to China and the East. For a century, as chaotic affairs in the Old World permitted, explorers tacked up and down our coast satisfied with no channel because all proved to be of fresh water.

As the seventeenth century dawned, a new train of interests was awakened and the rivers along our coasts began to be looked at for what they were—keys to a continent. For the true reason for this awakening we must unquestionably look to the Arctic Current which, meeting the Gulf Stream off the banks of Newfoundland, is shunted shoreward. Had it been forced seaward instead of shoreward a good deal of early American history might have been altered. The important zone of cod fisheries lay here in this Arctic Current immediately upon our coasts from Labrador to Montauk Point, Long Island. Probably this fishing zone had been more or less visited since the days of the Norse occupation of their "Wineland the Good," and long before Cabot. When Cartier achieved the "discovery" of the St. Lawrence, he found fishing ships already there.

Here is a period of romantic and important history of which practically every record has been lost. Now it was that colonies of fishermen occupied our coasts, found the waterway keys to it, and learned from the natives no small amount concerning the interior of the continent. The cessation of wars and rumors of wars in Europe at the beginning of the seventeenth century may not have had as much to do with the sudden awakening of interest in American discovery and colonization as the growing reports which passed from lip to lip, in a score of Old World fishing ports, of the new continent, its richness in cod and probably something of its flora, fauna, soils, and climate. It is questionable whether the work of Champlain, Raleigh, Weymouth, Gosnold, Smith, and Hudson would have been done in the timely fashion it was without this growing volume of testimony of innumerable fishing craft concerning the new land, its bays, inlets, good harbors, and rivers.

The zone of fishing "off the banks" had its marked economic effect in building up European fishing ports which supplied this trade with men, provisions, and tackle; these eventually surrendered something of their prestige when it became thoroughly established that equally good ports and harbors, in a fruitful land, were to be found on the spot. The contract into which the Pilgrims entered with the Virginia Company as to trade, trucking, and fishing, shows the purpose of founding on our shores new St. Malos and new Bristols—a project based largely if not wholly on the fishing industry and the acquaintance with our coast and its river-keys which opened up the land for the prosecution of the fur trade. Let us examine some of the aspects of river control as the first American settlements were made and their expansion began.

Chapter IV

SOME ASPECTS OF RIVER CONTROL

RIVERS exert control over the occupation of a continent only as they open doors into regions which man desires to occupy and exploit because of fertile soils and other economic considerations. These desires change through the years, as is illustrated by the signal neglect of the Mississippi by the Spaniards, who were obsessed by the passion for gold. As that great key to the continent seemed to open a way to no height of ground where gold might be found, they neglected it, so much so that we can almost say that the Mississippi was discovered by the way of the St. Lawrence leading to the empire of furs which were much desired. The Great Lakes region was pretty well known, and the Mississippi had been descended to its mouth almost a generation before the first little felucca ascended the "Father of Waters" in 1700.

From the standpoint of American occupation and expansion it is to be recognized that our northern Atlantic rivers, from the St. Croix to Chesapeake Bay, occupy quite generally northward-reaching valleys which run horizontal to the lines of precipitation and climate; also that to a degree they cross what were our colonies, now our states. In the building of our nation these considerations were of importance; they affect almost every problem relating to that period, favorably and unfavorably. Much emphasis has been properly laid on the problem mentioned in our last chapter—the service of river mouths and their harbors as sites of the first fishing stations and *entrepôts* of the fur trade and lumber interests. They gave a foothold on the continent. The question of the control which they exerted on further colonization and occupation has not been properly studied from the correlated standpoint of climate and soil. The New England rivers offered access only to a cold climate; upon the hundreds of newcomers who became acclimated during the first half century of testing, the rigors of this North had less effect; upon the thousands, however, who might have come the mere fact that the hurrying streams of this region afforded excellent sites for mills offered little compensation for the terms upon which a living was to be had, particularly to those chiefly interested in agriculture. To all such, length of growing seasons was an important argument for or against the occupation of any section. In a zone where a six-months winter was to follow a summer, either land must be greater in extent, or proportionately richer, than where a four-months winter reigned. All the rivers in this section were comparatively small, and their valleys rapidly grew narrow as men ascended them; while the Connecticut, the greatest of them all, with Yankee-like originality, broke away from its geological valley and, partly in consequence, received its first important migration by the overland trail from Massachusetts Bay.

Men dominated by the agricultural motive do not occupy to any great extent narrow river valleys, even when they consist of rich alluvial soil, if these cross isothermal lines at right angles. This is interestingly illustrated by the ancient inhabitants of America, the mound-building Indians. In the Middle West, the region where they flourished most extensively, the archaeological remains, which are the only indications of their habitat, follow isothermal lines rather than river courses, judging by the cultures unearthed[1]; they cross the Mississippi Valley, for instance, rather than going up and down it.

Occupation of river mouths and of the immediate valleys was the rule in New England. But, as will be brought out in detail in its proper place, the dominant factor in town-planting in New England was the fertility of the patches of meadow-land and intervales scattered across the whole land. The Massachusetts men at Haverhill gathered hay in the beaver meadows about Old Nutfield (Londonderry, New Hampshire) until the Scotch-Irish came and seized that prized inland region. The intervales where Concord, New Hampshire, now stands were first occupied by pioneers from Nutfield; they were ousted from this vantage point by Bay Colony men, but the latter were unable to dislodge them from the

---

[1] *Twelfth Annual Report, Bureau of Ethnology*, p. 526.

Nutfield meadows which the Scotch-Irish claimed under a New Hampshire "grant."

In the Concord case we have an illustration of the untoward conditions which arose at times from the fact that some of our rivers were intercolonial in character; this was marked in the case of the New England rivers which drained narrow colonies projecting horizontally from them to the far Pacific, as the Massachusetts and Connecticut. One has only to compare the James, for instance, which became Virginia's great highway of travel and commerce, to the Connecticut which, theoretically at least, was a highway to four rival colonies or sections. Had the Connecticut flowed lengthwise through Massachusetts or Connecticut its development as an important channel of trade and commerce might well have been wholly different from what it has been. River improvement, and canal and railway building, and all the economic advances brought by such development, have been seriously handicapped, if not utterly thwarted, by cases of interstate rivalry. These factors of material advancement (correlated closely with political homogeneity) have been accelerated in colonies or states whose territory trended along the line of national movement westward, particularly if such colonies had entire control of important river valleys.

This is interestingly illustrated as we cross the Berkshires from New England into New York. We find here a main northward-reaching artery, the Hudson River. The primary settlement at New Amsterdam at the mouth of the river and along its lower stretches, was typical of that of the northward-trending New England valleys. But in its possession of the Mohawk, the Hudson had a great westward-trending tributary. The inherent homogeneity of New York as a colony was founded on a principle intimately related to all factors of soil, climate, and geography, although politically it was based on a vague claim to a region occupied by the Five Nations on whose Long Houses was "stamped" the coat of arms of the Duke of York! The empire of the Iroquois had been laid according to natural principles of soil and climate; its boundary lines were also natural lines; it was watered by a central network of rivers and lakes; the physical boundaries were heights of ground or large lakes. Had the New York state which we know been split up into westward-stretching colonies or states, two of them having, let us say, the Mohawk for a boundary line, we would probably have seen the development of rivalries which would not have given that region its princely position of power in our national growth.

Practically all of these northern Atlantic rivers served at some point as boundary lines. This was a common Old World error perpetuated in the New. It led to many commercial and political handicaps. This has been poignantly illustrated by an excellent specialized study by the late Professor Bassett in his paper "The Influence of Coast Line and Rivers on North Carolina" which is cited at some length, not only as a type of the right kind of specific treatment of local geographical influence, comparable with the contributions of Fernald, Davidson, and McAdie, but also as a perfect illustration of the many ramifications which geographical influence may have.[2]

Professor Bassett pointed out that, in selecting rivers as boundary lines, the colonial fathers wrought unsuspected hardships on certain colonies and that much more colonial homogeneity could have been secured, both commercial and political, if heights of ground had been chosen rather than such rivers as the Potomac and Savannah. He shows that the valleys of the James and Cape Fear are centers of natural states, with Albemarle Sound the natural dividing line; that if Virginia had extended to this line, social order would have been established in North Carolina earlier and subsequent chaos avoided; and that if the Cape Fear had been the center of a colony it "would probably have been settled in the seventeenth century, and its southern frontier might have reached the Pamlico before the Virginia movement crossed the Albemarle Sound." Such a colony would have become distinctive and strong, and North Carolina, instead of being long under the hypnotic sway of Virginia-Albemarle influence, would have been independent of it.

[2] *Annual Report of the American Historical Association,* 1908, pp. 58–61.

It is difficult [writes Professor Bassett] to say what kind of a life would have developed in this southern region under independent conditions, but it is certain that life in Albemarle was very provincial. It was a province of a province. It was the most isolated part of the coast from the Savannah to the Penobscot. After 1730 its society became more orderly than before that time, but it was still wholesome, hearty, democratic, plain. There was a backwoods aristocracy, not only distinguishable as such because it was less democratic than the great mass of uneducated landholders around it. Intellectual leaders there were, as everywhere else in America, but their minds were formed by simple popular ideals, and taking economic and social ideals from Virginia they looked thither, also, for the politics which had to do with things larger than colony and state. Till long after the Revolution it delivered the political life of the state to Virginia leaders; and it was only the Jackson movement, through its strong appeal to the more democratic western and southwestern counties, which at last carried North Carolina for a presidential candidate who had not the support of Virginia.[3]

South of the Hudson, the Delaware and Susquehanna presented northward-leading valleys, famous first for the early settlements in the bays into which they flowed, second for the cross sections which they cut through regions of varying character, and third for serving as boundary lines to colonies to which they did everything except disunite them. Just as the little Westfield River was the one tributary of the Connecticut which made a groove for transportation westward from the Connecticut into the Berkshires toward New York, and just as the Mohawk served the Hudson similarly, so the Juniata was the westward-reaching tributary groove of the Susquehanna, later to be famous as a great canal and railway route.

These northern American rivers were of military importance in early days because they reached out their finger tips to or across international boundaries, offering strategic lines for wartime operations. By portage paths broken open in ancient days by great game animals and worn smooth by moccasined feet through generations, the Kennebec-Chaudière, Connecticut–St. Lawrence, Hudson–Lake Champlain, Mohawk-Oswego lines of communication

[3] *Ibid.*, pp. 60–61.

played a part in all colonial wars and are remembered well by the names of Arnold, Herkimer, Montgomery, Diskeau, Johnson, Abercrombie, Amherst, and Burgoyne. From the standpoint of expansion this fact has its significance. These valleys led to debatable and dangerous ground, and migration naturally went slowly along these lines of greatest resistance. The four fingers of the right hand represent the avenues which, though mere trails in some cases, saw the tomahawk and firebrand bring destruction and fear to outlying settlements. The relative size of the fingers also indicates the relative importance of the routes; the little finger stands for the Kennebec avenue; next comes the Connecticut route northward, branching in various directions toward the St. Lawrence; the middle finger by its size well represents the most important Hudson–Lake Champlain communication, famous for its campaigns in the Old French War, the Revolution, and the War of 1812–14; while the forefinger stands for the strategic Mohawk-Oswego-Niagara pathway.

On turning to the South we find an entirely new set of factors presented by the Potomac, the James, and the rivers of the Carolinas. It should be noted in the first place that, as we descend below Chesapeake Bay, the Appalachian mountain barrier trends noticeably toward the southwest, leaving here a constantly widening Atlantic plain, divided geologically into a lowland region and an upland region by the "Fall Line" which bounds the Piedmont and is marked in general by the cities of Trenton, Washington, Richmond, and Raleigh. Both the lowland or "tidewater" region and the Piedmont grow wider as we go south until below the last foothills of the southern Alleghenies or Unakas in the Atlanta region the Atlantic plain and the Gulf of Mexico plains merge together.

In their tidewater sections these southern rivers were, to a considerable degree, deep, slow-flowing streams navigable in certain cases up to the Fall Line (as to Washington and Richmond) and running from far inland in every instance. These rivers therefore gave not only an opportunity for settlement in the excellent harbors at their mouths but offered passageway for ocean-going vessels to the inland wharves of planters along all their lower reaches.

Again, these southern rivers occupied valleys which trended to a considerable degree parallel with the lines of precipitation, of climate, and of soil-series, although notable exceptions to this existed. Of more importance, however, was the fact that in general these valleys offered passageway in the westward direction which the American social movement was to take; and they had no recognized international boundary line lying at their head-waters. Several of these rivers lay within single colonies, notably the James. This made possible a degree of political homogeneity not otherwise possible.

Again, at the heads of some of these rivers, and just beyond the heads of all of them, was a rich "back of beyond," as the mountaineers of the upland South tersely expressed it. No inviting expanse of rich soils lay beyond the river valleys of the North until the Mohawk Valley was opened to migration in the nineteenth century. But to the westward of the Delaware, the Susquehanna, the Potomac's tributaries, the headwaters of the James, and beyond the head of the Broad, lay veritable garden spots. The control which these soils exerted on migration will be specifically dealt with later. What actually happens frequently defies logic and analysis; rivers "made" certain regions in the sense that they incited men to superlative energy because of the accessibility of good lands to which they led; in a sense they also laid handicaps on other sections. The unnavigable Susquehanna, leading to an agricultural El Dorado (the Pennsylvania Dutch country) and the navigable James, offering a highway to the earliest tobacco empire, make an interesting comparison, valuable because it clearly brings out the fact that geographical conditions are as nothing, in many instances, in the face of man's determination and activity. The belts of limestone soil west of Philadelphia and the Delaware were served by no navigable waterway. Such, however, was the royal quality of its soil that men quickly built "stone rivers" (roads) to meet Nature's lack; the result was, that while Virginia prospered famously with her rivers giving such kindly access to her fleets, those rivers themselves lessened interest in the development of other and much needed methods of transportation. But, on the other hand, inland Pennsylvania developed systems of transportation beyond anything known in the other colonies, bred in her wheat fields horses of nation-wide fame, built wagons to match her crops and very early set to work on canals. In her Lancaster County Fitch built his first steamboat, and Bucks County heard America's first steam engine chugging along her roads.

Thus two schools of transportation arose in these neighboring colonies which in a measure determined their outlook upon the regions behind them. Virginia thought of her West in terms of rivers, Pennsylvania in terms of roads and wagons; Governor Johnson and George Washington were famous exponents of the former, George Croghan and Conrad Weiser of the latter. The contest for the upper Ohio River commerce between these schools was spirited; one was essentially a tidewater, the other a stone road school.

Before we turn to examine the rivers of that area, another comparison should be drawn between regions so different in their waterway relationships with the outer world as Virginia and Pennsylvania. The tidewater country, because the individual planter had a personal touch with his overseas agents and merchants, was linked to the mother country as was no inland portion of any colony. This intimacy played its part in giving truth to the statement that Virginia was the "most loyal" colony; and it was above tidewater that disaffection soonest developed in the Old Dominion.

Throughout the Appalachian chain, and particularly in that portion of it known as the Alleghenies and Unakas, one discovers interesting relations of orography, the influence of mountains on mankind, to history. Much has been done to bring out the importance of heights of ground as factors in history. As specifically applied to this region our study falls into two classes; one deals with the effects of heights of ground on wind currents and thus merges instantly into climatology; the other emphasizes the handicaps to social movement laid by mountain barriers.

The Appalachians played no such marked part in altering climate as did the Pacific coast ranges, although their configuration operated to create zones, such as that of the Ashville region, which had a heavier rainfall than is common in the East. Lines shown on maps representing inches of precipitation and earliest frost in autumn and latest frost in spring are seen to have been influenced by the Appalachians and are somewhat diverted by them from an east-and-west course in conformity to the trend of the mountains; yet in the main, as we have frequently noted, their general direction is east and west. Amid the ranges themselves considerable climatic variation exists; this explains the popularity of the "coves" within those mountains; belts of soil on the mountain sides were found to be much influenced by climatic action not felt in the lower valley lands.

The direct influence of the Appalachians in blocking or diverting migration, is often described. Much is gained if the student maintains a balance and measures fully the compensations which these so-called "blocking" mountains offered.

We find that the drift of population toward the mountains was governed (so far as it was governed) by several factors. Automatically people moved toward unoccupied zones where good lands were cheaper or entirely free; men also looked to this region as their fathers, perhaps, had beheld this continent in the first instance as a land in which religious and political control would be less tedious; many also looked to such zones, as did Balboa and Daniel Boone, as conveniently separated from one's creditors. In some places, notably Virginia, it was easier to clear virgin soil than to fertilize worn-out lands; good soils everywhere exerted a drawing power, and some of the best land in the New World was found over against the Appalachian "barrier." No rule or law acted everywhere alike, and to lay down any except in specific areas of limited dimensions is not constructive.

In general the northern Alleghenies did not offer large bodies of good soil as did the southern; moreover French opposition developed strongly in the North, with its train of harassment from the Indian allies of France. And yet here no rule applies satisfactorily, because where the best understanding existed between red man and white (in New York) settlements were least extended, while where understanding was absent (as in Pennsylvania) migration became noticeable despite French opposition. As has been noted on another occasion, heights of mountains seem to bear no relationship to the social movement; a thousand factors operated—commercial, political, religious, economic.

Coming south to the Potomac and examining its watershed above the Fall Line (Washington, D.C.) several interesting problems present themselves. The river and its valley as we view it from Washington to Cumberland, Maryland, presented in the olden day many forbidding characteristics. The river bed was a succession of pools joined by noisy rapids; the main thoroughfares up the "valley," made famous by Gist, Washington, and Braddock, do not follow the river closely until Cumberland is approached. Two factors gave the Potomac its early importance. One of these was the key position of the Cumberland, Maryland, gateway to the Ohio at its head; the other was the great belt of limestone soil which, swinging down from the Delaware across Pennsylvania and Maryland, leaps the Potomac in the neighborhood of Harper's Ferry where the Shenandoah River marks the northern extremity of the far-famed valley of Virginia.

This belt of calcareous soil which forms the Cumberland Valley in Pennsylvania and the valley of Virginia, played an important part in American expansion and will be dealt with at length later. The northern branches of the Potomac which drained this part of Maryland and Pennsylvania, the Monocacy, Catoctin, Antietam, and especially Canococheogue should be particularly noted. They drain two splendid parallelograms of Maryland-Pennsylvania soil bounded on the east by Rarr's Ridge and on the west by Tuscarora Mountain and divided by South Mountain, the north extension of the Blue Ridge. A glance at a map shows, then, a remarkable focusing of lines of good soils and transportation on the Potomac between Harper's Ferry, West Virginia, and Williamsport, Maryland, where the belt of limestone spans the Potomac and swings southwest up that river's important southern tributaries.

With these facts in mind the two zones of the Potomac Valley—a tidewater zone and a limestone zone—separated by the section of the river between Washington and Harper's Ferry, well illustrate how a river may theoretically unlock provinces wholly different in character. However, we find here that the logic of events in no wise conforms to theory; the nature of the Potomac in this intervening section repelled rather than invited man's approach. The line of advance into the garden of the valley of Virginia was across instead of by way of the Potomac—coming from the Pennsylvania breeding ground of Scotch-Irish, German, Welsh, Huguenot, Irish, and English. To understand how Virginia developed sections so different as were her tidewater, Piedmont, and valley regions, we must see that the Potomac was not a guide to migration.

As we ascend the Potomac Valley and approach the main ranges of the Alleghenies we find that Wills Creek, focusing upon Cumberland, Maryland, gave access to a singular district of country and a passageway to the Ohio's chief tributaries and the Pittsburgh region. The interlocking of these Potomac and Ohio streams should be noted, but the important historical events which made them famous in the Old French War cannot be explained on the ground of favorable hydrography. An important trail crossing this divide had been laid by great game animals and worn deep by aborigines over this section of the Alleghenies between Pittsburgh and Cumberland. Its value to white men is, however, to be attributed to topography rather than to hydrography. In the Cumberland neighborhood the serried, glaciated Alleghenies gave way, and Deer Park, Mountain Lake Park, Great Meadows, Little Meadows, and the Glades of the Youghiogheny made migration easy through comparatively level open spots, often well watered, which produced grass and hay.

These singular oases within the mountains gave the upper Potomac its early power of control over exploratory, military, and migratory movements. These openings in the forests, their springs and rank grasses, were comparatively small, but they were veritable life-saving stations to man and beast because of the forage they afforded; they had been such to the buffalo, and the first traveler to pass through this region and leave adequate description of it (General Washington, 1784) noted particularly the buffalo roads which threaded it.[4] These meadows made the

---

[4] A. B. Hulbert, *Washington and the West,* pp. 67, 73.

thoroughfare the most satisfactory of any across the upper Alleghenies, and made possible a hopeful outcome of the venture undertaken by the Virginians who formed the Ohio Company in 1748—the undertaking which led to the opening hostilities of the Old French War in 1754. The strange anomaly of the outbreak of that struggle in one of these sunny open spaces on the finger tips of the Youghiogheny is better understood when the service of these patches of mountain grazing land, in a region where they were few, is taken into consideration.

South of the Potomac the numerous rivers present an interesting panorama from the points of view of both topography and historical association. Five important Potomac tributaries formed valleys reaching out like the fingers of one's hand toward the south and became zones of enterprising pioneering: the West Branch, South Branch, Patterson's Creek, the Opequon and the Shenandoah. Their interlocking with the tributaries of the Great Kanawha and James should be thoroughly understood in order to see the ground plan of the social movement which took place in the day when the Valley of Virginia received its first migration and when it became the thoroughfare to both Tennessee and Kentucky. The Shenandoah Valley reaches southward to the splendid Staunton region and almost touches the finger tips of the Cowpasture. It is plain what interesting grooves these valleys should make for a southwestern drift of population when the incentive came into existence; and unexcelled soils provided the necessary inducement.

One key to this panorama is presented by the hydrography of the James River. As we ascend through that bold gorge which the James cut for itself through the Blue Ridge—Balcony Falls—and view its headwaters, we see the Cowpasture and other tributaries present valleys reaching out to the head springs of the Shenandoah on the north. The passage over this strategic divide is made almost imperceptibly. On the south the valleys of the James's headwaters reach out toward the New River. This stream is significant because it takes its rise on the eastern side of the Allegheny divide, although being the main tributary of one of the Ohio's great feeders, the Great Kanawha. Thus the level lands, stretching north-

ward and southward, along the headwaters of the James were
perfectly formed to be a connecting link between the Shenandoah
and the New River. In its turn, the New, with its splendid soils,
offered passageway southwest; over the heights beyond it lay the
many fingers of the Tennessee. Those highlands are in reality the
summit of the Alleghenies, but so gradual is the rise that riding
swiftly by train or automobile one hardly realizes the mountain
barrier is being crossed; this is the "South Pass of the Rockies"
over the Alleghenies.

Beyond the headstreams of the New lie the rich limestone valleys (separated by mountain ranges) of the Watauga, Holston,
Clinch, and French Broad, which form the Tennessee. This connection between the drainage area of the Tennessee and that
of the tributaries of the James and New must be mastered, at
least in outline, if we are to understand thoroughly why such
names as Draper's Meadows, Watauga, Chiswell's Mine, Ingles
Ferry, Sycamore Shoals, Holston, King's Mountain, Nashville,
and Boonesborough became nationally famous. This is secured
by summing up our steps. Geologically the Cumberland Valley
of Pennsylvania swings down across the Potomac; the valley soils
stretch up the Potomac's southern tributaries, especially the Shenandoah; they continue on over the divide and are carried down
the two tributaries of the James; they then vault "the Alleghenies"
to the New River; in its tributaries they are still found, reaching
out into the highlands where the Tennessee's tributaries rise. Although this limestone pathway is everywhere cut into valleys and
slashed right and left into canyon-like gorges, at close intervals
lie splendid level tracts of land of varying dimensions, like those
about Staunton or Blacksburg, where Virginia located her Agricultural College. Moreover, the very mountains are often of a
type unheard of to the northward—with blue grass running at
times even to the summits of the "balds." Again, while following
the track of these limestone soils southward from Pennsylvania
and the Potomac, we have also been steadily climbing an upgrade
until, on the Tennessee table-land, we actually find ourselves in
a butter-and-cream and apple region quite similar to that of New
York far to the north; in passing toward a warm southern clime

the steadily ascending grade has neutralized the result. Climatically we have been standing still.

Nothing could bring out more plainly the controls exerted by this remarkable system of linking rivers upon the social movement which took place here than the recognition of the utter neglect which the social movement took of important rivers which offered barriers instead of holding out helping hands. Of this the Great Kanawha is a signal example. The ultimate goal of the immigration which came this way was, as is well known, Tennessee and the Ohio Valley. As it came over the Shenandoah heights into the Great Kanawha drainage (either by the Greenbriar or New) a short passageway to the Ohio and Kentucky was open by way of the Great Kanawha. The focusing of railways upon this strategic passageway today indicates what a key, hydrographically, it actually is. Yet the pioneer movement, guided by the unwritten lore of explorers and hunters shunned the gorges of the Great Kanawha and pressed on by the long but favorable route to the far-off goals by way of the New and the Tennessee's headwaters. Unfavorable Indian relations on the upper Ohio may have had their effect in driving the migration farther southward before it turned west. But the illustration of a famous gap and waterway passage being so completely ignored as was the Great Kanawha, has its value in showing that topography alone is often unimportant in the matter of social control in the face of soil factors of magnetic power.

In summarizing this matter which is, however, not to be understood without a careful examination of the appended maps, we see that in the North the rivers served as controls over expansion into their own immediate drainage systems, and for the most part independently of each other, while in the region south of the Potomac there was one great "river" of soil (paralleling the Ohio very closely) stretching from Tennessee to the Potomac—with carrying places, one over the portages between the Shenandoah and Cowpasture, another across the divide to the New, and a third across another divide to the heads of the Tennessee. That this was not one "river" but many, and that the so-called portages were numerous was more than compensated for by the inviting, fertile lands to which this passageway gave access. What magnetizing power it exerted remains to be examined as we go on.

Any careful diagnosis of the Alleghenies and Unakas from all points of the historical horizon, geographical, hydrographical, and edaphic, must bring one to the conclusion that the notion that they were serious barriers to migration is not tenable. The student of history knows that where they gave way entirely (as in central New York) social movement advanced more slowly than anywhere else, and where they were high and widest of all (as in the Cumberland Gap route) population advanced most rapidly in the crucial generation, 1760–1790. Indian, and French and Indian opposition had a basis of operations determined by other factors than those of orography. They had a marked influence in making the Southwest the line of least resistance. The mountain fastnesses assisted these enemies in their work of destruction and pillage by covering their operations and hindering pursuit.

But the river systems and the soil of the river valleys of the Southwest marked out inviting lines of least resistance which would not have been ignored had there been no opposition to the northward. It is believed that a consideration of facts, developed as we proceed, will lead the candid person to agree that the social movement to western Virginia, Tennessee, and Kentucky would have been approximately what it was had there been no French or Indian opposition at the north.

Chapter V

HIGHLAND PATHWAYS OF CONQUEST AND MIGRATION

While our rivers were of primary importance as keys to this continent, making possible secure vantages at their mouths and along their lower stretches for the original settlements of colonists and forming lines of least elevation for advances into the interior, a salient basis for an understanding of the process of conquest and migration is missed if we ignore the key heights of ground which were everywhere found as American expansion went on. The exact routes—though their study often illumines many passages of our history—are not so important as the contemplation of the pattern on which they were marked out, the analysis from the point of view of the influence of watersheds.

The average person is not discerning when all rivers are adjudged of equal value as factors in disseminating our pioneer agriculturists. Attention to the landward thoroughfares is particularly helpful in bringing out the correct relative importance of the waterways, both in the tidewater and upland regions. We have just seen three peculiar types of river control, those exerted by the Potomac, the Great Kanawha, and the Shenandoah-James-New line of communication. An analysis of the land routes which complemented these water avenues goes far to explain their peculiarities in actually affecting migration. The student must differentiate between rivers which were navigable and those which were not; the latter may have drained a remarkably fertile area to which they did not "lead" in the sense of offering a navigable highway, as in the case of the Connecticut and Susquehanna; or, as in the case of the Potomac, a river may have a famous tidewater section, drain another rich zone to which it does not "lead" in the sense of navigability and yet, finally, point out a strategic portage such as that found beyond the Cumberland, Maryland, region. Under such circumstances a river is often best interpreted by the land routes which complement it.

The "pathless wilderness" is a dearly cherished figment of the American imagination. The expression is used glibly, and many pictures illustrate our histories and other volumes relating to pioneer days showing the pioneer forging forward into a trackless forest. The author has looked for vestiges of these in northwest and northeast Canada, along the whole chain of the Alleghenies from Williamsport, Pennsylvania, to Atlanta, Georgia, along the line of the Rockies from Union Pass to Apache Pass, in Michigan, Oregon, Louisiana, Texas, France, and China, without success.

Before the time of the historic Indian, before the day when the bison tore open his great roads on his annual migrations, the "wilderness" of America was covered with trails. A glance at any one of the Bureau of Ethnology maps of the remains of the first Americans (mounds, cairns, etc.) will show that while these mound-building Indians lived beside waterways they also inhabited to a considerable extent the fertile uplands which are not drained by navigable streams. Any thoughtful contemplation of the conditions which existed when forests covered this land, when no swamp or bog had been drained, and when the flood plunder of generations filled the river valleys furnishes a basis for understanding what these highlands meant to the first Americans. The contents of their mounds prove that they did not know the bison, that first heavy game animal who was a migratory traveler and whose highland trails have ever been a guide to safe, high ground; the bones of practically all other animals which we know are found in those mounds except those of this valuable beast. Yet along the watersheds on which the transcontinental buffalo and Indian trails were afterward opened, we find mute suggestions that these earliest of peoples knew them well and used them. Their remains are found beside some of the most strategic gaps in our mountain ranges. As has been remarked on another occasion, the mounds indicate that this race tended to migrate along isothermal lines as the cultures (technique of workmanship) within the mounds which cross the Mississippi, for instance, prove. This line of movement across the east and west backbone of Ohio, since made famous for its modern lines of fast steam transportation, is plainly marked. No one has ventured to mark out these lines of probable movement, save in one instance, but in that case the line quite perfectly follows the great modern routes of travel running westward from the Buffalo, New York, region.[1]

With the coming of the bison our watersheds were his natural passageways from feeding ground to feeding ground; here he was safest from his most treacherous foes, bogs and quicksands; here his trails suffered least from erosion; here forest growths were lightest and their *débris* least interfered with the right of way; here sunlight encouraged the growth of the grasses he loved. Everywhere the broad roads of the buffalo converged from watershed and highland upon the meadow regions and salt licks and wallows which were his favorite habitat. The first white men to enter Kentucky found these roads wide enough to give thoroughfare to three wagons moving abreast. The pathways of the moose, elk, and deer, although they were not migrants, were laid out with the same unerring instinct. It is to be noted, too, that these trails led almost without exception to the open lands which at a later date were to be most prized by the white emigrant because most easily cultivated.

Thus if there had been no Indians in the whole region between the Blue Ridge and the Great Plains of the West our forefathers would have found a marvelous network of thoroughfares laid out with a canniness of which the railroad engineer's tripod has again and again approved most strikingly—and all of them focusing somewhere upon excellent, well-watered, cleared ground, in the shape of glades, natural meadows, beaver meadows, or intervales. A pathless wilderness was the last thing our pioneers wished to enter; it meant, without fail, no springs, no grazing grounds easily conquered by the plow, no salt, no game.

It is very much worth while for the student of history to mount this vantage point and catch the picture of American migration from the heights where the first Americans walked and where the bison roamed. When the white man came he found these watershed

---

[1] *Twelfth Annual Report Bureau of Ethnology;* cf. Thomas map of prehistorical routes, McGee and Thomas, *Prehistoric North America,* pp. 2–3.

routes the main Indian thoroughfares of the continent; branching
from them in many directions ran the lesser pathways to hunting
grounds, village sites, fishing grounds, and regions occupied by
friendly and hostile tribes; but the main thoroughfares in America
were undoubtedly the same in far-off centuries as when Europeans
first looked down their vistas in the sixteenth century. The longest
dividing ridges still held their preëminence as the safest courses
through the tangle of mountain and swamp; the safest fords of
one century were unquestionably the safest fords of another. The
regions to which the main trails ran, the meadows, glades, and
intervales in which the bison delighted, were favorite sites of Indian hunting and agriculture.

These pathways were the greatest asset bequeathed by the red
man to the first Europeans who entered our continent, untrained
for the task of continental mastery. They not only led to the best
spots for human occupation, but they also marked out the transcontinental lines upon which explorers should advance, the pathways upon which armies should march, the routes of first "ridge
roads" and, in many cases, the lines upon which trade and commerce should flow until the day when, perhaps, the air shall become the main channel of communication. Pioneers ascending river
valleys found, at the heads of these, direct, deeply worn portage
paths to the waterways across the divide. Rare was it that these,
if much trodden in the past, were not also much traveled by the
newcomer; rarer still that those little worn proved of any more
moment to the white man than they had to the Indians, or to the
animals which, in most instances, preceded the red men there.

In a general way the main thoroughfares of the eastern portion
of our country have been outlined and described.[2] These may be
loosely divided into three general classes: valley trails, watershed
trails, and portage paths. Doubtless undue credit has been given
to our rivers as pathways into the interior of the continent and
too little to these land passageways. The study of any of our lesser
river valleys, as well as the perusal of earlier pioneer documents,
brings out the character of these valley troughs as of little value

---

[2] A. B. Hulbert, *Historic Highways of America*, Vols. I–VIII.

in most cases in furthering actual migration, although they were invaluable for affording water for man and beast.

The watershed highways were, doubtless, of first importance in opening up the interior of the land. The study of these routes and the science of finding the dividing ridge (as the art of determining the strategic highland in any section may be called), becomes interesting to the lover of the out of doors. The accuracy by which these paths were laid is graphically described by Hon. Charles Augustus Murray, one of the first foreigners to be impressed by this lost art of the frontier:

On the 18th we pursued our course, north by east. . . . In the first place, it enabled me to keep along the dividing ridge; an advantage so great, and so well understood by all prairie travellers, that it is worth making a circuit of several miles a day to keep it; and the Indian trails which we have crossed since our residence in the wilderness convince me that the savages pay the greatest attention to this matter. . . . The "dividing ridge" of a district is that which, while it is, as it were, the backbone of the range of which it forms a part, heads at the same time all the transverse ravines, whether on the right hand or on the left, and thereby spares to the traveller an infinity of toilsome ascent and descent.[3]

This phase of the history of transportation can be studied in any locality, and it makes a theme replete with interest. Footprints, especially if the same path be traced and retraced for any length of time, may leave a record for an astonishingly long period, particularly in a region of plenteous rainfall like our eastern United States. Water settles in the track; vegetation disappears; even on the summits of steep hills ancient pathways are still visible. The routes of famous old-time roads, although not used for a century, are often plainly to be seen at many points. One may stand on the National Road where it lies above Washington's battlefield at Fort Necessity and see, a mile away across the meadows the plain track of Braddock's Road on the hillside beyond, although for a century that hillside has been under cultivation. In the forests, east or west from that point, the roadway is marked in places by great gorges eight and ten feet deep where

[3] *Travels in North America*, II, 29.

lagoons formed along the track in wet seasons, killing vegetation except the rankest grasses.

There is perhaps not a township in any of our counties in which the study of these watershed and other routes does not throw new light on the story of pioneer discovery and occupation. In many cases the important routes of today exactly coincide with those of centuries ago, and the hill towns so familiar, for instance, in New England, show in a general way the alignment of the old-time ridge road which followed very closely the Indian trail. To those who are inclined to pursue antiquarian research of this character the old sites of ferries, more or less clearly defined in the early legislation of any colony or state, will be found to be a reliable guide by which to locate the ancient routes. Infallibly the ferries will mark the strategic points where the ancient trails descended from high ground to the fords. These were usually located on a river at the mouth of a leading tributary. The sediment of this tributary was deposited below its mouth in the main river, making the water shallower at that point and therefore more easily forded. About such fords human habitations naturally sprang up in the shape of trading cabins, villages, or forts. As vehicles began coming over the old routes and ferries became necessary, these were located near by, either above or below the ford. Blacksmith shops and other emporiums of trade normally appeared at such spots, and were followed very frequently by primitive towns. As railways followed the valleys of streams in most cases, such spots as those occupied by the old fords were the first ones to be bridged by railways since the water was shallower at that point. Thus the village near by may easily have become a city in another century. This has at least been the rule in hundreds of cases.

The student of American history who becomes acquainted with the uplands of his neighborhood is in the way not only of understanding better just how population advanced and was distributed, but is likely to assay other factors of geography, of soils, forests, and vegetation as he never would otherwise. He will recognize the old spring sites which exerted such a control over travel in the early day.

In fine, one must become familiar as best one can in this modern day with the highland environment in which the American pioneer so largely moved, if one is to grasp the essentials of pioneer history. Local history can be made interesting to the dullest class by taking it up from this point of view; and in the act, the influences of geology, of topography, of soils, forests, and vegetation can be analyzed to vivify and illumine what is so often considered a threadbare and humdrum theme. How wide are the ramifications of interest which may thus be invoked is illustrated when we consider these land routes as pathways of conquest and migration.

The old keys to the interior of the continent are found whenever we study any one of the long dividing ridges and mark the important portage paths which crossed them. Reviewing again the cross-country journey we made from the Atlantic to the Mississippi from this standpoint, the reader will recall the great number of crossroads which were passed at such vital points as between Fort Edward, New York, and Lake George, between Rome, New York, and Wood Creek, and near Lake Chautauqua, Akron, Ohio, Fort Wayne, Indiana, South Bend, Indiana, Chicago, Illinois, and Portage, Wisconsin. The strategic nature of these sites is illustrated by the many pioneer forts erected at such points. In part both of the lines of communication, highland and river, are today followed by railways and this gives one reason for the modern importance of such cities as Akron, Fort Wayne, South Bend, and Chicago in the railway age.

All this was true in the far day when Oldham crossed the Connecticut path from Massachusetts Bay to New England's rich valley, or when La Salle felt out the portage from the Maumee to the Wabash, or the St. Joseph to the Kankakee which were the links in the empire chain that he sought to forge between the basins of the St. Lawrence and the Mississippi. To man the country and fortify it in that day meant, in part, the manning and fortifying of these narrow but mighty cross trails where river routes and highland routes crossed. It explains not only the rise here of fortifications but the appearance, as well, of mission chapels, traders' cabins, and often the beginning of settlements which grew into towns and cities. In the later phase of this development canal building came to occupy an important part, since these waterways for the most part followed river valleys. In reaching out from one to another the ancient portage path was usually metamorphosed into a water pathway. One pleasure of the railway traveler of today, whose thoughts are faring backward across the years to the day when men were struggling with their rude task of continental mastery, is to note the art by which the surveyor's tripod has conquered the details of finding the pathway of least resistance in any hilly or mountainous section of the country, especially in seeking a pathway for the rails from one river valley over the divide to another. The streams which the engine is following become a silver thread; the laboring of the locomotive is noticeable as the watershed is approached; and when you boom suddenly into a tunnel the reflection comes that this very point, perhaps one spot out of a score, has been approved by science and experience as the most practicable either from the standpoint of grades or the relatively smaller cost of maintenance. Yet in many instances, if you should leave the train as it emerges from the tunnel and climb the height which it has pierced, you would find on its summit the main pathway through the selfsame region carved out centuries ago by the hoofs of bison or moose whose instinct was as unerring as the tripod's magic.

This point of view is useful to the student who desires to understand the era of the conquest and occupation of the American colonies. As Professor Davidson followed the tracks of Ulloa, Cabrillo, Ferrelo, and Drake, and endeavored to put himself in their places, "understanding the seasons and the difficulties they encountered," and trying "to follow them day by day in their exciting discoveries," so it is quite worth while for any student, with the system of the inland thoroughfares of our country in mind, to put himself, so to speak, in the shoes of Champlain, La Salle, Céloron, Johnson, Washington, Braddock, and Burgoyne, and study their campaigns from that highland vantage.

As we follow these men in their "exciting discoveries" we find ourselves threading, in large part, the Indian thoroughfares on high ground. A lack of understanding of such location of marching parties and armies has led to a failure to get the essentials of much pioneer campaigning, the most perfect illustration of which is seen in Braddock's annihilation near Fort Duquesne. Many a book has pictured Braddock's force as entrapped in low ground, with his enemies firing upon him from advantageous heights. Reverse this picture and one has the exact fact. Braddock had been following in the main Nemacolin's Path, the chief trail through the Cumberland-Pittsburgh region. When it dropped into the Monongahela Valley, Braddock floundered about prodigiously in attempting to find another pathway which would lead by higher ground to his objective. A study of his track shows his effort to find to the northward the highland trail to the junction of the Allegheny and Monongahela which was so successfully traversed three years later by his fortunate successor, General Forbes. Failing to find the desired route, Braddock reluctantly came around into the Monongahela Valley. Upon crossing the river his vanguard proceeded up the ridge or "hog-back" by which the trail led to a long height of ground flanked by parallel ravines. The enemy, hoping to block his passage of the Monongahela, were too late; they were as fully surprised as was Braddock. Instantly they adopted perhaps the oldest and most common piece of Indian strategy in war—to seize the two ravines and hem the foe in on the high ground between them. Lying thus on their bellies in the underbrush of the slopes they offered no mark to the English or colonial rifles while, plainly silhouetted against the sky above them, the advancing army huddled together on the trail. So long as they remained stationary, not a French or Indian rifle could easily miss its mark. The position of the attacking party explains why so many of the British-Colonial force asserted that they never saw one of their assailants. The unwillingness of Braddock to retreat, and his inability to go by the blood-red vortex on the trail where rifles from both ravines and a height to the right focused, left his men to be slaughtered in their tracks. Had he adopted either alternative, and maintained morale, he could not have been defeated.

The same tactics lost and won many a known and unknown forest *mêlée*, notably the sore defeat of the Kentuckians at fatal Blue Licks, the victory of the mountaineers at famous King's Mountain, General Lewis' conquest of Cornstalk at Point Pleasant, and Burgoyne's memorable defeat at Saratoga.

Again, this highland point of vantage is valuable to all who care
to assay anew the factors that played a vital part in the era of
migration which followed close upon the heels of the era of conquest. Yet as a matter of fact, these two eras overlapped in a way
which has not been fully appreciated. To a degree insufficiently
emphasized, these so-called armies of conquest were also armies
of exploration.

In a day when most campaigners were agriculturists by trade,
perhaps never a party or army marched into "the enemies' country" which was not a beast with a thousand eyes, intent upon the
manner of country coming into its range of vision. As new hills
and valleys broke upon the view, the topic of commonest remark
(next to the immediate question at hand) was of the soils, the
springs, the forests, the growths which were revealed. Men were
led constantly to compare the new lands thus invaded with the
old lands at home, to estimate on the basis of their experience what
could be raised here better than on their own lands, and to dream
dreams of another kind of conquest that they sometimes promised
each other to make when the enemy had been driven from his forts
and lairs. Every telltale sign of rich soils was noted and well remembered.

When Ludlow of Windsor, Connecticut, was pursuing the recalcitrant Pequots, he took note and cherished the memory of the
fine meadows where Fairfield, Connecticut, now stands; and no
sooner was the war over than he migrated to the spot and built his
future home. Washington never forgot that Allegheny meadow in
which he fought his first battle and signed his first and only capitu-
lation. As soon as the opportunity presented itself he acquired that
tract along with many others which he either saw during his western campaigns or of which he was reliably informed. It is undoubtedly true that most returning colonials were asked concerning
the character of the regions they had visited the very moment the
story of the campaign was off their lips. Even harried, escaping
captives who only dared travel at night did not fail to note and
report the nature of the country through which they passed and
upon which they looked, no doubt, with unconcealed interest from
their daytime hiding places. The wary Yankee, Joseph Petty, flee-

ing from Montreal during Queen Anne's War, was such a one;
and from his covert in the rich Missisquoi Valley in Vermont he
saw enough to enable him to report: "There is extraodoary good
land on each side of this River all ye way as far as we could perceive." In later days in the Far West the same thing was true
as, for example, in the case of the Kentucky trapper, Wolfskill,
who became in 1831 the pioneer American orange grower at Los
Angeles, California.

When we recognize the character of the routes followed by these
colonial armies, when we realize how inevitably they were led by
highland or lowland trails to the very keys of the continent's interior, and how those trails had been laid out in part to link up
the most fruitful meadows and intervales which would instantly
command the attention of men predominantly farmers, fresh reasons present themselves for studying these pathways from sociological standpoints.

When the struggle for mastery of the frontier ended, the ancient
passageways instantly became the avenues of advance for armies
of migration which were guided to an extent we cannot begin to
measure by the men who had gone that way before on an earlier
mission. Into northern New England and across toward central
New York, and out from the teeming centers of the middle and
southern colonies to the Allegheny valleys and gaps streamed this
mightier army, turning Indian trails into ridge roads and occupying glade, meadow, and intervale. Many factors as we shall see
influenced this, the most important conquest of the continent. It
is for us here only to note that it was no "pathless wilderness"
which men undertook to conquer, but that innumerable routes,
wisely chosen in the first instance, offered passageway into every
district into which men had good reason for going. And, as the
regions which seem to have been most popular with the first far-off
Americans were, at a later date, undoubtedly most popular with
the later Indians, so, too, those same regions became most popular
with the white inheritors of the continent and remained so until
the advent of the age of commerce and great cities.

The study of our topic here is, however, valuable only as generalizations are avoided and as concrete examination of specific

instances absorbs the student's attention. Local history is considered by many a threadbare and hackneyed theme. And yet the fact remains that there is hardly a county in the United States whose history cannot very well be rewritten, and interestingly so, by those who will approach the subject from the standpoint of topography, geology, soils, climate, forestry, vegetation, and upland and lowland lines of land and water communications. Suggestions for examining certain of these factors have been given in preceding pages; others concerning the control exerted by soils and vegetation will be given in succeeding pages. For the study of the topography of any region (which should be the preliminary work) there are at hand the excellent topographical maps issued by the United States Geological Survey, by means of which a complete knowledge of the drainage of every region so far covered by these surveys may be had and the main watersheds and divides accurately plotted. Side by side with these should be placed the earliest contemporary maps illustrating explorations, military campaigns, and pioneer settlements.[4]

In connection with these cartographical materials the student should get into close touch with the geological, agricultural, and botanical departments of his state, or with the nearest local institution where data relating to the soils, flora, and fauna of the region to be studied can be secured. As will be shown in succeeding pages, he should know his region's soils and forests as well as its topography and history.

[4] Maps of land company settlements and surveyors' records in local court and state houses and historical societies will be found invaluable. The largest collection of manuscript maps relating to the early history of our East and Middle West is to be found in the British Museum and Public Record Office. Some eight hundred of these have been reproduced in A. B. Hulbert, *Crown Collection of American Maps*, Series I, II, and III.

Chapter VI

THE STORY OF OUR SOILS

WITH the foregoing necessary considerations of American geography in mind—for our rivers were the main avenues of social movement—we turn now to an examination of soil and soil provinces as they relate to geography.

The surface of the globe is made up of rock, soil, and humus. Most rocks, except limestone, expand and contract alike in all their parts. As rock expands, water and rootlets enter it, and the result is annihilation of the rock and the formation of soil. Rocks may also be reduced to soil by the action of glaciers and of wind. Some soils remain upon the parent rock and are accordingly known as sedentary soils, as those on our rock plains or slightly inclined plateaus, or in the granite region of the Southern Alleghenies or in the "black prairies" of our cotton states. Colluvial soils are those formed by erosion of mixed *débris,* while alluvial soils are the finer soils which are washed away and which form the rich valley lands so noted for their fertility. The attention given in preceding pages to river valleys was therefore of twofold consequence to our theme.

Our national Bureau of Soils has to date surveyed about one hundred million of our two billion acres of soil. As this work advances, many interesting facts have come to light; and while it is early to forecast others, or correctly to interpret the lessons which will come from this important work, some facts already have been revealed. An instance is the relationship of certain soil series to isothermal lines and the constant recurrence of similar types of soil across the wide expanse of our United States. The Miami series of soils is an example. This series has had a very important influence on American development; it is found at intervals from Massachusetts on the Atlantic to Washington on the Pacific. So, to a degree, are other strong, safe soils which have early acquired and will long keep a superior reputation.

The Bureau of Soils divides our soils into five main classes. Residual soils are found in many parts of the country. They are formed from the framework (limestone) of the shells and bones of marine and fresh water animals which gives a soil area fertility by the leaching out of the lime, expelling from the soil carbonic acid. If we saw no benefit in the long domination over our wide interior of the great inland sea hitherto mentioned, and its constant connection either with the Arctic Ocean on the north and the Antarctic on the south, for ages being replenished with their myriad forms of aquatic life, the important part played by our residual soils in national development helps us now to do so. For to that age-long and seemingly eccentric phase of the great plan of continent building, we may be grateful for our magnificent western wheat fields and for the surprising fertility of the supposedly arid deserts which, at the touch of water, have been found to be as imaginary as were the "pathless" wildernesses—being rendered fruitful because of the marine life which once existed over their wide expanse.

Our sandstone soils are found in the eastern part of the United States; they are known as "poor sand soil" and include the sand hummocks of Florida, the long-leafed pine lands of the southern states, and the "pine barrens" of New Jersey, New York, and Michigan. These soils often furnished a useful foothold for settlements, but became sterile after brief cultivation. While the South had more than its share of sandy soil, it was also handicapped with a large acreage of putty soil, notoriously refractory, composed of a powdery sediment known provincially as "crayfish" land. On the other hand the South had its invaluable acres of "buckshot" soils which made the Yazoo Bottoms famous in our agricultural history. These soils were calcareous, that is, formed of the shells and bones of marine life, the name being derived from the crumbling which took place when it was wet. So rich were some of these buckshot lands that a thousand pounds of cotton lint have been raised on a single acre in a virgin state, and from three to four hundred pounds on acres which have been under cultivation for a generation.

Humus, or soil formed from vegetable *débris,* is common to all regions outside the arid. It is noted for turning black upon being wet; its depth is commensurate with the roots of vegetation which it supports.

A bird's-eye view of the soils of the United States presents a wonderful panorama, both in variety and distribution. As a nation's great wealth is in its soils, our wealth is magnificently strewn across the lines of longitude. We are just beginning to learn the dynamic power of this soil inheritance. Its real meaning becomes plainer as the soil surveys of our Bureau of Soils proceed; and as the responsibility of the ownership of this inheritance comes closer home to us in the shape of world appeals for help, the work of the survey and classification conducted steadily by our Bureau takes on a genuine significance.

Soils favorable to grains were, fortunately, strewn across the whole nation. Not only do the famous Hagerstown and Clarksville soils bring forth wheat now as readily as they did when the Palatinate Germans and Scotch-Irish made Pennsylvania our first granary in William Penn's day, but beyond them the Chester and Penn soils of the upland regions proved fair grain-growing soils, while the unguessed Marshall, Miller, Miami, and Wabash soils of the Middle West proved that the mound-building Indians chose well the seat of their empire. Finally, the Fargo and Marshall soils of the Northwest have, in recent times, opened a whole new era in the history of the world's wheat market. The pathway of the McCormick reaper, fashioned in one of those little valley streaks of calcareous soil stretching down from Pennsylvania across the Potomac, has gone westward parallel with the course of the "Star of Empire," broadening out the trail as it ran; and we are rapidly learning that even the "deserts" can be made to grow grain.

Our corn lands, well known to the red man, were the mainstay of our early pioneer colonies in the New World; they were found to have an unguessed extent when Americans began the march to the Pacific; they grew wider when the Alleghenies were spanned until the renowned "corn belt" was reached where the Marshall, Miller, Miami, and Wabash soils surged out to their full extent, creating a provincial region which, through its swine and cattle, makes a large impression on world trade.

Until lately we have thought our fruit lands were measurably isolated and limited, with the Dunkirk soils of the Lake Plains and the Placentia soils of the Pacific coast marking the regions of highest productivity. But in these later days the fruit-bearing qualities of the Porter and Cecil soils in the supposedly barren Appalachian highland wastes have proven their importance; their wide extent bids fair to make their products a large item in the future national fruit market.

The part played by our cotton and tobacco soils is well understood; the empire of Crockett and Laredo soils for lowland cotton, and the wealth of Houston, Orangeburg, Wabash, and Miami soils in the uplands, made cotton "king" in a sense no one expected when only the Norfolk soils of the Atlantic sea islands were giving to the pioneers in the industry their feathery wealth of stalk and boll. In these same lowland soils, especially the Laredo, sugar cane, corn, and tobacco luxuriated, enabling this provincial realm to meet a nation's need and so to bring in the wealth which gave to its feudal barons and petty kings place and character and an influence on national affairs which was powerful if sectional. New England's sterile hills and fast-running streams were no less sectional in their inducement to industrial development.

Elsewhere we shall examine the influence of certain of these soil series in their respective zones. For the moment our attention needs to be focused on the outstanding fact of the wide distribution of our important soil series; hardly one was thoroughly provincial, although certain members of some series may have been so; but our important soils came early to bear definite reputations, however little their chemical composition was understood. They were known by their colors or by vegetation which became typical of them, known by their almost universal reaction to weather conditions and erosive influences as well as by their ability to withstand drought, turn water, or recoup themselves after constant tilling, or by their inability to withstand toxic influences.

The study of the soil map issued by our Bureau of Soils presents to the inquirer many interesting problems; while we are warned that the map is tentative and intended to be suggestive rather than authoritative, it yet brings out very clearly certain facts which are, or ought to be, of interest to the historian.[1] In Section 1 of the subdivision of the Coffey map we find six soil zones in the northeastern portion of the United States. The timbered New England–New York region stands out emphatically, marking in general the glaciated region with which we have dealt, with the patches of Ontario or Lacustrine soils—famous for their fruit—plainly marked in the north. Anticipating for a moment a topic to receive attention later, one cannot but note that if men were so influenced by a soil-and-climate environment that soil lines became the lines of least resistance in migrating, this section of our map indicates that the New Englander had a fairly straight pathway westward through New York to Ohio.

To the southward the eye immediately catches the position of the "Shenandoah Group" of soils which, we have seen, had so interesting a part in our study of the Potomac's and Tennessee's hydrography. When those curving prongs are recognized as consisting of the finest land for general agriculture in the eastern portion of our country, as well as the pathway of one of our most famous movements of American migration, their relationship to the Piedmont sandstones and shale soils takes on a new significance. In general they accurately mark that Shenandoah-James-New-Tennessee line of river communication which, as heretofore brought out, meant so much in luring to the Southwest the first western migration. In passing, the reader may well note how very generally the Fall Line actually serves as a boundary line between two wholly different soil provinces.

Section 2 shows the "New England of the West" from the soil-forest point of view, in which the interesting islands of Ontario soils form peculiar caps on western Lake Erie, Saginaw Bay, Green Bay, and Lake Superior. The largest of these, in the Toledo region, is well remembered by the student of western history for the high degree of agriculture among the Indians found here when General Wayne won the memorable battle of Fallen Timber on the Maumee. The drawing of the forest and prairie lines in the upper Mississippi Basin shown here attracts our attention. The

[1] "Preliminary Soil Map of the United States" by George N. Coffey (1911). (Milton Whitney, *Soils of the United States*, U.S. Bureau of Soils, Bulletin No. 55.)

prong of prairie soil, wind-laid soils chiefly loessial, begins near Logansport, Indiana, and widens abruptly as the Illinois line is crossed; except for the many arms of the Mississippi which intervene, these soils stretch straight westward into Nebraska with eccentric flares into South Dakota at the north and into western Kansas and Colorado at the south.

Turning to Section 3 we are looking at the old "Gulf of Mexico" which formerly reached up to the present junction of the Ohio and Mississippi rivers. From that point southward we see, in the broad strip of loessial and alluvial soils bordering the Mississippi, what that river has done with the aid of the Arkansas and the Red to break the continuity of the broad layers of soil which crossed this part of the country, in addition to the prairie lands above mentioned. We also have here the extension of the "Shenandoah Group" of soils leading to the famous limestone oases in which lie Nashville, Tennessee, and Lexington, Kentucky. The relation between these TLSh soils may well be noted carefully. Their influence on migration was marked; more vividly than on most maps we see here the character of the intervening spaces of indifferent soil past which the migration would go, leaving behind the "mountain whites." The position of the Cumberland River in its narrow prong of limestone soil may well be remarked carefully with reference to Cumberland Gap. It will be seen to lead directly to the great island of limestone soil about Nashville; and as that region was a famous hunting ground we see plainly how the "Long Hunters" and other adventurers came to it very naturally through Cumberland Gap.

As a type of local investigation of the relation of soils to social development a question arises, upon noting that interesting finger of limestone in northern Alabama just south of the Florence, Alabama, region. It is seen to lie in the country which is said to have seceded from Alabama during the Civil War, to have formed a local government, and to have issued a currency of its own. Does this island of limestone in the midst of a slate and shale country help to explain such an exotic political plant here? Again, do the curious islands of marine soils running from central Alabama northwest into Mississippi explain equally curious social, political, agricultural, or industrial phenomena in those states? These particular inquiries may prove to be wide of any useful mark; but the recognition of such factors ought to lead to the rewriting of much local pioneer history, as will be shown by specific instances.

Section 4 of the Coffey map is interesting from several points of view, only one of which will be noted for the moment. That is the close relationship of Charleston, South Carolina, to the Piedmont region about Columbia, through which the Fall Line passes. No southern port of importance had so close a connection with the upland. In addition to this proximity, a fine body of Orangeburg soil intervened between the immediate tidewater region and the Fall Line which, as we shall see, was a magnet of migration. All this makes plainer the important line of advance from Charleston to the inland expanses. The Scotch-Irish migration (carrying with it such families as the Jacksons) from Charleston along the Rutherfordton Trace to our first "empire of free grass" joined, in the Watauga district, the other famous line of movement from Pennsylvania up the Shenandoah and along the forking tributaries of the James.

As we enter the great Northwest in Section 5 we pass from the light-colored timbered soils and the area of light-colored prairie soils to the arid regions—from the wooded portion of our East to the unforested Great Plains. Numerous explanations for this treeless empire have been offered, Professor Shaler's being most widely accepted: that the Indians burned the forests in order to start the fresh shoots which drew the game animals. This explanation, however, seems to the writer to take too little account of the age-long incompatibility of association between trees and grass. If such prairie burnings had been going on for centuries, as Shaler's theory supposes, would we have found an entirely different kind of native vegetation on the black soils of the Marshall series from that found on the light soils of the Miami series? In certain soils, grass and trees fight tremendous battles for supremacy, grass sometimes being victorious and sometimes vanquished.[2] The map shows the western boundary of timber-growing soils. On these soils, fires do not destroy forests and no amount of burning would

[2] Whitney, *op. cit.*, p. 37.

change the soil into "prairie sod." On the latter soil in its natural state, real forests are not found. The explanation of our treeless plains must, therefore, go back to the factors of rock, soil, and climate which determined vegetation.

The various belts or islands of soils in this middle zone, such as that in which Concordia, Kansas, stands, help very largely in interpreting the later American migration into this region, and might well be studied locally along lines suggested in our later chapters. Their influences on town location, railway building, etc., were dominant. The great patches of undifferentiated western timbered soils are seen to be all but joined in Wyoming, where lies the famous South Pass key through the Rockies—the interesting region where the finger tips of the Platte, Missouri, Colorado, and Columbia rivers so nearly touch.

As we take up our Southwest we see that the diversity of soils in the arid and semiarid region of the North extends to the Rio Grande. Those long tongues of soil reaching up out of Texas fascinate the student; and their influence on the American advance in the days when Austin and Houston were laying the beginnings of Texas, as will be shown, were important. Lines of social movement upon the northward-stretching belts of marine soil attract attention; the one reaching from near the Red River beyond the San Antonio River is particularly interesting; it includes the cities of Dallas, Corsicanna, Waco, and San Antonio, while just over a narrow streak of Atlantic soils lies thriving Fort Worth on its tongue of undifferentiated limestone widening to the southward while the marine belt narrows almost to a point. By comparing this with Section 3, the important relationship of Louisiana to Texas soils is recognized; across this zone the sweep of the cotton plant from the Old South became a factor of national importance. Another phase of Texas history is placed in a clearer light by a better knowledge of these soils and precipitation lines; that is the northward movement of the great cattle drives.

The forested and unforested regions of the Pacific coast area present a theme too generalized to be treated here. However, reference to the soil map will serve a useful purpose as we take up other themes presented by our subject.

Chapter VII

SOILS AND MIGRATION

FACTORS presented by our soil provinces and soil series must be recognized if the early story of American migration is to be completely understood; while this applies particularly to the early generations of the period of American development when most men were agriculturists, it also has a significance continuing throughout our entire history as a nation down to the present time.

Our fathers became acquainted with certain types of soil and vegetation in their first New World environments, in their New England, Virginian, or Pennsylvanian settlements; they learned what might be expected of soils under varying climatic conditions, learned how to cultivate them for the best profit, and mastered to a degree the arts of raising on them crops, flocks, and herds. They became familiar with the growths of weed, shrub, and tree which these home-soils produced, and early differentiated between those which were valuable and should be encouraged and those which were harmful to man and beast and should be eradicated. Particularly did they come to know the trees and the varying qualities of their woods and products. Much of this lore the Old World emigrants brought with them; doubtless some information was picked up from the aborigines;[1] but it was by experience, not by intuition, that men learned that osage made better wagon-wheel spokes than hickory. In all the industry of the old-time farm or plantation the wood with which the farmer or planter became acquainted was a prime factor in the development of his establishment. Especially was this true in the arts of home and barn building, and in the making of a hundred and one utensils and tools, in the furniture for the home, and in barn, workshop, dairy, orchard, and granary. Thus it happened that men came to feel at home in definite soil-and-vegetation environments which they

[1] This item, what newcomers to our land learned in woodcraft from the Indians, has been overlooked. See William and Mary College *Quarterly*, October, 1910.

knew; this type of local sentiment went so far that the general run of pioneers knew exactly where on the farm the root or herb needed in the sick room was to be found and how it was to be prepared. This was so well understood by enterprising land speculators that, in their prospectuses concerning new lands, we find glowing accounts of the pharmaceutical bounties of lands offered for sale as for instance, an abundance of dog fennel or mayweed, the "sure cure" for malaria!

These facts are not new but their influences, in the day when the eastern settlements were sending the best of their lifeblood into the West, should be accorded more complete recognition than is common. When John Pyncheon went from Massachusetts Bay to the Connecticut and returned home again, what were the first questions put to him by the citizens of Roxbury? The very ones that were put to Daniel Boone on his return from Kentucky, to Moses Cleaveland on his return from the Western Reserve, to Lewis and Clark on their return from the Columbia and the Pacific: "What of the soils?" "What do they produce?" "Could we master the land there by the tricks of the trade we have learned here at home?"

In taking these factors into consideration, we must hold fast to the lesson learned at the outset and recognize that there were always important expelling forces provocative of migration in every instance, as well as the subtle, mesmeric influences which good soil and favorable environment exerted. Sometimes limited or sterile soils played a part as an expelling force; in the vast majority of cases, however, economic, social, political, and religious motives were the fundamental influences. It is only as we maintain an honest balance in this matter and avoid being "possessed with the devil of one idea" that we are fitted properly to assay the control exerted by the soil-and-vegetation factors. To overlook the former would be fatal; to overlook the latter forbids taking into our range of vision factors of undeniable value in explaining the vagaries and eccentricities of the American advance to the Pacific.

Not until very recently has much attention been paid to soil composition. In the old days there were good, homespun theories, tested and proved by the experience of mankind everywhere; and, in fact, these have changed little with the introduction of scientific classification and nomenclature. As of old, soils are still commonly known by their colors and by the types of vegetation, generally by the trees, which they produce. Deep-seated affinities for certain soils existed in the blood of European emigrants; queer antipathies and prejudices, some of which required rectification, were not uncommon among them. Nature played some queer tricks on men who put too great faith in past experience, as certain Quakers discovered when they tried to cultivate worthless black soil in southwestern Pennsylvania. In turn, prejudices acquired in the Atlantic seaboard zones of occupation, as in New England or Virginia, were found to need readjustment by the grandsons or great-grandsons of the European emigrants as they in turn crossed their "Atlantic Ocean" (the Piedmont region) and pressed on into the American West. The same soils reacted differently to agriculture in different climates. The lesson which early Virginians learned to their sorrow—that virgin Virginia soil produced wheat which was all stock and no head—was found to work in the opposite way when the Blue Ridge was crossed. In some cases an almost imperceptible rise in altitude was not counted at its true worth, as the men who ascended the Shenandoah Valley learned when, far to the south, they suddenly found themselves in a New York butter and cream country on the table-lands of the Southern Alleghenies.

However, most of the old laws usually held absolutely true, and much of the Old World lore and of the Atlantic seaboard experience served the pioneering American in good stead as he sought his destiny on western lands. Among these stocks of knowledge, that concerning the color of soils usually held good. Black soils, composed mostly of humus, were almost everywhere good soils. Instances in which this was not true furnished newcomers with the surprise of their lives; but practically everywhere black soils, with their content of lime in the form of carbonate, equaled or exceeded expectations. Next to black soils, red were most desirable; crystalline rocks bred red soils, the color being produced by the weathering of hornblende or iron rust (ferric hydrate). These were usually well-drained soils; when not well drained the color disappeared, warning off men of experience who had learned the comparative sterility of white "crayfish" soil which lacked both iron rust and humus.

Vegetation produced by soils was, however, a truer guide than color, for the reason that the latter remained much the same at various altitudes and along the various lines of precipitation, whereas the natural growths showed not only just what the soils produced but what the same soil produced in different positions with respect to the sun, at different altitudes and in different isothermal zones. They showed plainly the effects of plenteous rainfall or sunlight, and also the effects of long or short growing seasons between the latest frost in spring and the first in the autumn. Some of the eccentricities of early migrations and the planting of early settlements (not in the least understood until now) become plain and significant as the relationships of temperature and soils are better understood. Guided by infallible laws governing vegetation—for you cannot fool all blue grass any of the time or any of it all the time—men, wise beyond their century, chose what was best from the lavish bounty of Nature. If you ask our Weather Bureau for an explanation of the Scotch-Irishman's aversion to limestone soil, you will learn that "other things being equal, it is probably safe to say that frost is more liable to occur over a heavy soil than over one of lighter character, in which more or less sand forms a constituent part." An explanation of the settlement of the "coves" of the Alleghenies is to be found in the fact that what are called "frostless belts" lie around the sides of the hills or mountains where longer growing seasons were found than in the valley bottoms. The cove settlements had their basic reason for existence in facts not at the time couched in modern scientific phraseology but founded on solid principles recognized by vegetation. The relative amount of moisture in soils is commonly indicated by the size of trees; often trees of like species, growing only thirty or forty feet apart in the same soil, develop so differently (due to unequal moisture supply) that the inexperienced person can hardly be persuaded that they are of the same species. Trees, like men, sometimes migrate to soils which they particularly cherish, as in the case of lowland growths in the South such as the tulip, black walnut, and Kentucky coffee tree which migrated up into calcareous soil when opportunity permitted. Examples of this migration are evident on Cave Hill in Mississippi and on tributaries of the Mississippi River.

So, while soil colors were not ignored, soils came to bear definite reputations from the trees which grew on them, and are still so known by all who have not acquired the terminology lately adopted by scientists. "Piney soil," "white oak land," "chestnut oak soil," "hickory bottoms," and "hackberry hummocks" are all commonplace terms. Even regions which were known for their grasses took from them their names as the "blue grass" or "penny-rile" regions of Kentucky; while the intervales and meadows in the East, the glades of the Alleghenies, and the prairie country of the West, all indicate certain types of unforested land.

East of the Rockies trees were common criteria for judging soils, and the oak, of which there are fifty species on either side of the Rockies—not one of which has crossed those ranges to the other side—has played an important function in our history as a herald of good and bad land. The black, white, post, black-jack, willow, Spanish, and live oak served in many parts of the country as an indication of soil qualities, grading higher in pro-portion to hickory, and lower in proportion to pine; yet whatever the mixture, thick growth usually indicated good soil and thin growth poor soil. The willow oak, for instance, on undrained soil has the appearance of an apple tree, while on drained uplands it is a stately indicator of good soil. The post oak in the "flat woods" stands only from ten to twenty feet high; in prairie country it often runs from fifty to seventy feet in height.

The nut-bearing trees were excellent guides to good land, the hickory, as has been noted, being a true criterion of the relative value of "oak openings" and oak prairies. There were, however, "disappointing hickories" such as the pignut, mockernut, and whiteheart, whose warning was well heeded by the intelligent pioneer. Post oak and black-jack prairies served the same purpose of warning pioneers away from some portions of the Mississippi Valley states, just as the dwarfed elms flamed out a similar warning in the flood plains of the Red River Valley, bespeaking heavy, waxy, gumbo soil, gray and white crayfishy bottoms, and "benches" poor in lime phosphates and humus. These soils also produced scrubby water oaks, willow oaks, and cypress.

Land speculators played skilfully on the credulity of prospective eastern buyers who had an abiding faith in "oak soil," for as we have seen, there were oaks and oaks, some of them growing on very inferior land. In the East, oak soil bore an excellent reputation, but to the westward the scrub, willow, and post oak thrived on anything but rich soil; black-jack and post oak were not as common in the Middle West as in Alabama and Mississippi, but wherever found, they had the same characteristics—they were dwarfed on yellow clay. The common "post oak flats," bordering many streams in Indiana and Illinois heralded noncalcareous soils poor for grains. Hickory grew, however, much finer on the loamy uplands of Illinois than on identical soil in Mississippi and Alabama, because of drainage and climate factors. The blue ash always indicated rich soils in the Mississippi Valley and in the coves of the Great Smoky Mountains.

The yellow loam uplands of Illinois were identical in character with the brown loam uplands of Mississippi. It was immediately obvious where these mediocre soils gave way to calcareous soils, with the appearance of growths such as the linden, wild cherry, and ash on high ground, ash, walnut, and butternut on lower levels, and sycamore in the valley bottoms.

In the South the cotton plant was an infallible guide to good, calcareous soils, although it too could play tricks on those who judged wholly by superficial appearances. One field might produce stalks ten or twelve feet high and yet bear no blooms; while in an adjoining field, stalks not half so high might be thickly covered with blooms and bolls. In the West the juniper tree was found to be well worth watching as a true indicator of calcareous soil; so also was the sunflower plant a guide to calcareous soil on the Illinois prairies, being replaced, on cultivation, by the luxuriant ragweed. In the middle states Yankees recognized the New England aster as a pillar of cloud seldom or never failing to indicate good land; the clover plant served the same purpose, pointing out soils good for wheat. In the South the devil's shoestring, on the other hand, served as a reliable warning of poor soil, and its disappearance was an indication of limestone which it could not endure. Among other plants in the prairie country the polar plant, prairie plant, swamp rose mallow, and wild indigo all indicated soils above the average.

The literature of land companies and the journals of surveyors and travelers are filled with statistics concerning the girths of trees in many regions. Sharpers took advantage of this, too, in luring purchasers and immigrants to certain districts, for the rule did not hold everywhere alike. The biggest trees in the far West by no means indicated the richest soil. But to the average Yankee or Virginian the record of the sycamore that Washington measured on the Ohio in 1770 spoke volumes, and the general acceptance of his measurement is evidence that Parson Weems's fanciful cherry tree tale gave Washington a reputation for honesty which the reverend author of the tale never deserved. The tree mentioned lacked three inches of being forty-five feet in circumference at a height of five feet above the ground. Yet the Johnston Elm at Johnston, Connecticut, measured forty-one feet in circumference, one foot from the ground; but there was no comparison between the fertility of the soils from which these trees sprang.

It is worth while to picture in imagination the marvelous drama of Nature presented in those far-off days when vegetation spread across the longitudes, every tree and grass blade forging ahead or drawing back or making a stunted compromise with soil and climate according to the laws of natural selection. To some slight degree—worth an attention never given it—the same thing took place in the early days of our development when soil was the prime matter of interest to the vast majority of Americans.

There remains to be written the story of the conquest of the oak tree in America, or that of the age-long struggle of the tender blue grass to master an empire severed by many mountain chains—the story of those drifting seeds, falling on dry, rocky, or fertile soil, fighting a battle to the death with rivals, following blind alleys, pursuing box cañons, hopelessly crossing isothermal dead-lines, and yet always bringing forth types conforming to their various environments. In such a study of the migration of plant communities, in the diagnosis of their battles and battlegrounds, and in the geographical, topographical, climatic, and edaphic factors which governed their conquests and defeats, we see the process which, in a different and fainter way, was repeated in the days when most men were agriculturists and the watchword was "Westward Ho." If we honestly recognize that the expelling influences were often wholly paramount, if we appreciate that in all human advance the rule of "hit or miss" was the common one and that to lay down any other may be rashness—then are we prepared to recognize that the factors of soil control were present and in many cases were of commanding importance.

An advocate of the theory of influences of the soil on man who was wholly unafraid of the "devil of one idea" would find unalloyed delight in the brilliant if unscientific outbursts of the late Senator J. J. Ingalls of Kansas in favor of blue grass as a panacea for most ailments of society. The quotation here appended is interesting as an example of the error of imputing causation to things which are inert (Professor Burr's warning p. 2) and because a real truth lies between Ingalls' lines, namely, that the results of supplanting prairie with blue grass gave men new opportunities which, if seized upon, brought revolutionary social results:

There is a portion of Kentucky known as the "Blue Grass Region," and it is safe to say that it has been the arena of the most magnificent intellectual and physical development that has been witnessed among men or animals upon the American continent, or perhaps upon the whole face of the world. All these marvels are attributable as directly to the potential influence of blue grass as day and night to the revolution of the earth. Eradicate it, substitute for it the scrawny herbage of impoverished barrens, and in a single generation man and beast would alike degenerate into a common decay. . . . The salutary panacea is blue grass. This is the healing catholicon, the strengthening plaster, the verdant cataplasm, efficient alike in the Materia Medica of Nature and of morals. Seed the country down to blue grass and the reformation would begin. Such a change must be gradual. One generation would not witness it, but three would see it accomplished. The first symptom would be an undefined uneasiness along the creeks, in the rotten eruption of cottonwood hovels near the grist-mill and the blacksmith's shop at the fork of the roads, following by a "toting" of plunder into the "bow-dark" wagon and an exodus of "out West." . . .

Though Kansas is embryonic and foetal at present, it is not difficult to perceive certain distinctive features indigenous to our limits. The social order is anomalous. The appetite of the community demands the stimulus of revolution. It hungers for excitement. Its favorite apostles and prophets have been the howling dervishes of statesmanship and religion. Every new theory seeks Kansas as its tentative point, sure of partisans and disciples. Our life is intense in every expression. We pass instantaneously from tremendous energy to the most inert and sluggish torpor. There is no golden mean. We act first and think afterwards. These idiosyncrasies are rapidly becoming typical, and unless modified by the general introduction of blue grass, may be rendered permanent. . . .

Under these benign influences, prairie grass is disappearing. The various breeds of cattle, hogs, and horses are improving. The culture of orchards and vineyards yields more certain returns. A richer, healthier, and more varied diet is replacing the side-meat and corn-pone of antiquity. *Blue grass is marching into the bowels of the land without impediment.* Its perennial verdure already clothes the bluffs and uplands along the streams, its spongy sward retaining the moisture of the earth, preventing the annual scarifications by fire, promoting the growth of forests, and elevating the nature of man.

Supplementing this material improvement is an evident advance in manners and morals. The little log schoolhouse is replaced by magnificent structures furnished with every educational appliance. Churches multiply. The commercial element has disappeared from politics. The intellectual standard of the press has advanced, and with the general diffusion of blue grass, we may reasonably anticipate a career of unexampled and enduring prosperity.[2]

Practically speaking, long interstate series of good soils, peculiar prejudices brought from afar as to soils and agriculture, and finally reports of adventures in the interior of our land, exerted very positive influences on migration. As illustrations of the first mentioned influence, the Pontotoc Ridge in Mississippi and the Chennenugga Ridge in Alabama may be cited as lines of social movement dictated by lengthy stretches of good lands. That rich

[2] Cf. *Missouri Historical Review,* April, 1912, for another chapter in blue grass history in the West.

province of calcareous prairie soil in Louisiana, which breaks across the Texas line to its fullest dimensions, was a vital factor in the story of the interstate phases of the expansion of slavery. The black prairie land of Indiana, which spread out widely across the Illinois line, and the "Chestnut Country" in southern New Hampshire which Massachusetts men were so prompt to occupy, are further illustrations of these interstate soil influences.

Now and then curious instances of peoples' settling in an environment similar to that which nurtured their fathers, although geographically the two zones are widely separated by wholly different types of country, is illustrated in the case of the "Hillbillies" of the Ozarks in Miller County, Missouri, and their peaceful penetration of a region so like their Cumberland plateau of Tennessee and Kentucky which their forefathers loved.[3] Such illustrations should be awarded an attention in the interpretation of local history which is not commonly given them.

So, as has been pointed out, should the predilections and affinities shown by immigrants to this country for certain types of environment and soils. The success of the Palatinate Germans in Pennsylvania was remarkable when compared with numerous other colonies of these same people who did not happen upon a part of America that resembled the Rhineland limestone soil in their original home. The peculiar prejudice of the Scotch-Irish against limestone soils, which were looked upon with disfavor in Scotland where they were known as "dry lands," was a factor which played no slight part in depositing that rugged race of pioneers on the frontier of frontiers behind Pennsylvania and Virginia—the empire of slate and shale. Though the basis of this prejudice was soon found to be erroneous, it was effective at the beginning as a factor (but not so important a one as poverty) in placing many of the

[3] F. V. Emerson, "A Colluvial Soil and Its People," *Bulletin of the American Geographical Society*, XLVI, No. 9, 655.

The enthusiast, fully possessed with "the devil of one idea," might draw from Nature a parallel between plants moving northward from their zone of highest temporary development and the experiments of races moving in that direction in the effort to acquire Nordic characteristics. The data for plant life are given us by A. A. Crozier. In so migrating, plants become dwarfed in habit; are more fruitful and more highly colored; their leaf surface is increased, form modified, composition changed, period of growth shortened; they acquire the ability to develop at a lower temperature. (*Biological Gazette*, X, Nos. 9, 10 [September and October, 1885], 373.)

newcomers on the outer border of these colonies. Others of their race were naturally drawn to the same locality through clan and family influences.

Finally, pioneer literature is filled with evidence that reports of soils and vegetation sent back by early adventurers into our American West had a marked influence on migration. All reports—whether coming to Massachusetts Bay men from the Connecticut valley, to Connecticut men from central New York, to New Yorkers from Illinois, or to Illinois men from Missouri or California—were studied in the light of common experiences and knowledge. If soils reported were of a familiar character, the effect was mesmeric; if strange soils and vegetation were reported, it was negative. In the former case prospective emigrants knew something of what to expect, whether the home-building, crop-raising, and other tools which they knew how to make and use masterfully would be the tools they could employ in the land of promise toward the setting sun.

The psychic influences of such reports were perfectly understood by all associations and speculators which were interested in developing western land purchases, as in the case of the Ohio Company of Associates, the Holland Land Company and the Transylvania Company. In the original declaration for instance, of the Ohio Company, the "underwriters" state:

> that from personal inspection, together with other incontested evidences, they are fully satisfied that the Lands in that quarter are of a much better quality than any other known to New England people—that the Climate, seasons, produce, &c. are in fact equal to the most flattering accounts which have ever been published of them.[4] . . .

As a result, one great bugbear of pulling up stakes and removing to a distant home was greatly neutralized by this comfortable feeling that, however great the distance and the consequent toil, men knew toward what kind of haven they were faring and that they would meet there conditions which they had mastered before. This not only lessened the terrors by the way but doubtless in no

[4] A. B. Hulbert (ed.), *The Records of the Ohio Company*, I, 2.

small measure was an inducement for women to accompany the men.

So natural science is valuable in pointing out the way for the explanation and clarification of history; an instance of the use of such evidence is D. W. Johnson's study entitled "The Biological Evidence of River Capture."[5]

As we shall see later, the famous blue grass region of Kentucky was not appreciated at first by the early explorers and pioneers; to them the canebrakes, which promised to afford such luxuriant feed for cattle, made the strongest appeal. This diverted the attention of explorers and surveyors to relatively poor soil. Cane had meant much to the Indians; calcareous soil nothing. And so when George Yeager, who as an Indian captive had gone to the Kentucky cane lands to hunt with his captors, later took Simon Kenton and John Strader in 1771 to find rich lands in that region, they searched for cane and missing it, returned disappointed.[6] Four years later, however, Kenton found cane "upon the richest land they had ever seen" near Maysville, Kentucky, where he later established Kenton's Station. The far richer blue grass region was in this case overlooked because the Indian hunter-nomad basis of civilization was different from that of the coming European agriculturist.

Side lights like this, which in no small measure aid in understanding history, lie in these biological-agricultural relationships. We should be as alive to the possibilities of the case as was High P. Coultis when he wrote his illuminating paper on the racial phase of the introduction of hard wheat into Kansas. Overlooking historical inaccuracies, which are adventitious, this story is of genuine interest and importance:

It has been commonly believed that hard Russian or "Turkey" winter wheat, as a product, was unknown in Kansas before the advent of the Mennonite settlers in the early '70s; but, although the Mennonites were perhaps most largely instrumental in introducing this variety into the state and the greatest factor in its early development, they were not the first who raised it. At the time Bernard Warkentin, late of Newton, a

---

[5] Bulletin of the American Geographical Society, XXXVII (1905), 154.
[6] R. H. Collins, History of Kentucky, I, 17.

Mennonite from Russia, came to Kansas, in the year before the first party of Mennonites from the Crimea district of Russia emigrated to this state, there was a small colony of French settlers in Marion county who were raising the hard winter wheat, although not to any great extent. Indeed, wheat was raised in such small quantities in that section of the state that Mr. Warkentin, who had built a water-power mill on the Little Arkansas river, at Halstead, Harvey county, was compelled to ship wheat from Atchison to supply his mill.

In 1783 the Crimea and the provinces adjoining were ceded to Russia by the Turkish government as conquered territory, and Catherine II of Russia, in casting about for colonists to settle in the newly acquired country, decided to invite the people of a Christian sect known as Mennonites, then inhabitants of western Prussia, though formerly from the Netherlands, as being most desirable. The Mennonites were known as a very thrifty and industrious people; in fact, they were accounted among Prussia's better class of agriculturists. Many inducements were offered them to emigrate to southern Russia, some of the concessions being religious freedom, immunity from military service (their doctrine is one of nonresistance and noncombativeness), and a land grant of about 160 acres to each family.

Catherine hoped that the Mennonites would serve as a pattern for the indolent tribes scattered over southern Russia and that they would intermarry with these tribes, but she was destined to be disappointed, for the immigrants kept to themselves and never intermarried with the Russians.

Many Mennonites went to Russia on the terms offered and settled just north of the Crimea, in what is known as the Molotschna (or Milk river) colonies. Here they engaged in agriculture, raising wheat mostly, as the grain best adapted to that locality. At first they raised the soft spring wheat, and it was not until about 1860 or thereabouts that the hard winter wheat which was raised exclusively in the Crimea, was introduced into the Milk river colonies, largely through the efforts of Mr. Warkentin, father of Bernard Warkentin, the pioneer miller of Harvey county, Kansas. In a few years this Crimean wheat was raised there exclusively.

The success and continued prosperity of the Mennonites had caused a feeling of jealousy among the native Russians and the tribes in southern Russia and they were desirous that the many special privileges granted the Mennonites should be withdrawn, and to this end they importuned the government. These privileges had been promised for one century, or until 1883, but the Franco-Prussian war, in 1870 and 1871, afforded the Russian government a loophole of escape, and a treaty was entered into with Germany, whereby Russia was to remain neutral during the war provided Germany withdrew the political guardianship it had exercised over the three million or more German colonists in Russia. These terms were accepted by Germany, with the proviso that the Germans should be allowed ten years in which to emigrate, if they saw fit to do so, rather than become Russian subjects.

About this time (1872) the Atchison, Topeka & Santa Fe Railroad Company had completed its line through Kansas, thus earning the three million acres of land granted by the national government to the state of Kansas to aid in the construction of a railroad from Atchison in a southwesterly direction to the west line of the state, and had organized its land department for the sale and peopling of the lands so acquired.

The land department of the railroad, knowing of conditions in southern Russia, was extremely anxious to turn the tide of this desirable immigration Kansasward. To this end, C. B. Schmidt, immigration agent of the company, was sent as a missionary to open the eyes of the Mennonites to the desirability of Kansas as a place for home-making and for the successful carrying on of the pursuits which had brought them prosperity in their adopted land.

Prior to Mr. Schmidt's departure for Russia, however, in August of 1873, five Mennonite leaders—Jacob Buller, Leonard Suderman, Wm. Ewert, Rev. Deitrich Gaeffert, and Heinrich Richert—visited the United States with a view to finding the most suitable location for their coreligionists. After visiting Kansas, Nebraska, Dakota, Minnesota and Manitoba, they decided upon Kansas as the most desirable state, and the counties of Harvey, Sedgwick, Reno, Marion and McPherson as those best adapted to their agricultural pursuits. The soil and climatic conditions of this locality were more similar to the steppes of Russia than any other section they visited. Bernard Warkentin was associated with the Santa Fe railroad immigration department, and was stationed at New York to meet his countrymen and direct them to Kansas. One large party of Mennonites, an entire shipload, numbering perhaps 1,000, demanded tickets to Nebraska, but they were dissatisfied there, and through the efforts of Messrs. Schmidt and Warkentin, they were induced to come to Kansas, where they located in Marion county. In October of 1874 the Mennonites bought 100,000 acres of land from the railroad company. During 1874 and 1875 the flow of Mennonite immigration into Kansas continued, and in the summer of 1876 it was estimated that there were over 6,000 of these people located in the Arkansas valley or contiguous territory.

Among all the Mennonites who came from Russia there was not a single illiterate person. As a rule, too, they were all in good circumstances financially, some even buying land by the section. Individuals among them had as much as $40,000 or $50,000 each.

The first party which came to Kansas brought, all told, not more than twenty or thirty bushels of seed wheat, of the Russian or "Turkey" variety, which had been most popular with them in their Russian home. The conditions in the portion of Kansas settled by them were ideal for the introduction of that particular wheat. The grain did not have to become acclimated as was the case when it was introduced into the Milk river colonies north of the Crimea. On account of its wonderful adaptability to Kansas, the colonists soon found themselves possessed of all the seed necessary. Just at this time, too, the milling industry of the state was changing from the burr to the roller system, and with this change the problem, of grinding the hard wheat, which could not be done satisfactorily by the burr system, was solved.

The first importation of the Russian or "Turkey" hard red winter wheat into Kansas from the Crimea which was available and for sale to the general public was made by Mr. Warkentin in 1885 or 1886.[7]

[7] "The Introduction and Development of Hard Red Winter Wheat in Kansas," Kansas State Board of Agriculture *Report*, No. 155.

Chapter VIII

THE MEADOWS OF NEW ENGLAND

WITHIN proper limitations it may be said that there was one preëminently important thread of migration in the early history of American expansion. That line is represented in the migration of Abraham Lincoln's ancestry—from Massachusetts to New Jersey to Pennsylvania to the Valley of Virginia to Kentucky to Illinois. The ground plan of this movement is made plain for the most part by the study of the river valleys to which we have heretofore devoted a degree of attention, the reason for which at last becomes plain. It is now our purpose, first, to examine with care soil factors which influenced the planting of the more important of social zones along this line of march, and second, to estimate the effect of the same factors in projecting and guiding migration by this southwesterly pathway through the Cumberland Gap into the strategic Blue Grass Region of Kentucky on the lower Ohio and the Mississippi rivers. Beyond that potential zone of American frontier life, represented loosely as stretching from Louisville to St. Louis, no one area of expansion plays a similarly predominant part in the lusty drama of advance to the Gulf and the Pacific; but to the radiating trails from that Mississippi Valley sector to Texas, California, and Oregon, from the standpoint of our text, attention will finally be given.

But whether of one zone or avenue or another, it is hoped that our approach and treatment will suggest a whole field of activity which can be made to revivify the study of local history in many of our states. For in every effort to secure historical clarification from natural history sources, the more concrete the application the more constructive the result.

The legend runs that when the Creator had finished his plan of fashioning the earth he sent angels forth from high heaven to report progress in the success of the undertaking. When their findings were rendered it appeared that the task had been well done except for an oversight in the matter of providing soil for Norway and Sweden. Those provinces were practically barren rock. To remedy this deficiency a Royal order went forth to sweep heaven and scatter its dust upon "the lands which God forgot." The peasants of those countries cherish still this pretty story and, in consequence, call their soil "the dust of heaven."

New England was not wholly forgotten in the matter of soil at the outset, but it is not certain how she would have fared but for that mighty afterthought of creation, the advance of the ice sheets which enveloped her from the North.

The Alpine mountains which, previous to the Ice Age, marked this zone were crumbled by the ice sheet covering that portion of our land, and the soil is largely composed of the crushed rock of those mountains. But, as if to make amends for this heritage of very indifferent "dust of heaven," there was granted to New England a bounteous supply of rapid rivers, and during the centuries which followed the withdrawal of the ice packs, these streams carved out their narrow valleys and filled those troughs with excellent alluvial soil. The annual freshets of these swift streams drove out from the valleys much of the heavy growths and deposited fresh layers of soil every year. Here in the valleys the forests were much more open than elsewhere and this allowed the sunlight to come in. The freshets likewise created and supplied water for the numerous swamps and bogs which were of considerable importance to the future New England.

These age-long processes meant a great deal in fitting this granite region to be the home of aborigine and European. In the more or less open valleys of rich soil sprang up the meadows for which New England has been famous; here even the crudest methods of agriculture known to the red man brought some return in crops of maize and vegetables. The swamps likewise were of value because they furnished an almost limitless quantity of rank grasses and flag for mats, and thatch for houses, and, if they were drained, made excellent meadows.

The beaver aided in no small measure in this meadow-making process. This sturdy animal must be reckoned one of the real workers in the background of New England's history, as well as

an economic factor in the beginnings of her trade. By damming
the streams the beaver caused water to back up; here in the still
pools not only was the silt of the streams deposited, but the water
killed off much forest growth. As these dams were abandoned,
or as the beavers were destroyed, the flooded areas, enriched by
the fertile soil formed largely from the silt, came up to grass, thus
making the "beaver meadows" which are found in every zone
which was the animal's habitat. From the standpoint of the future
population, the value of the beavers' work lay in its wide distribution and the consequent extent of the meadows brought into
existence. Here again, it is proper to mention a service which a
historically minded zoölogist may perform by more carefully
charting the beaver zones. These meadows which the beaver enlarged or created became, as we shall see, magnetic attractors of
migration. This influence of the beavers was felt across our whole
country. In the main they thrived best among tree growths which
indicated good soils. In the search for this animal some of the
richest of western lands were thus first explored and made known.

We shall probably never have any reliable data on the extent
of Indian agriculture. When the white man reached America the
Indians had from time immemorial been tilling the more open
valley and upland meadows, clearing the land by frequent burnings and probably by girdling trees which would not succumb
readily until dried up. The valleys, because they were automatically fertilized by floods and because they were freest of forest
growths, served the red man best. Yet they tilled not only the
richest valleys but the good interior lands, such as the excellent
land about Woodstock, Connecticut, whence came the corn that
tided the Puritans at Massachusetts Bay over their first winter.
There is a curious relationship between good soils and our Indian
wars. But neither from this source, nor any other, is it probable
that we shall learn much concerning the amount of land which
the Indian tilled; many facts point to the conclusion, however,
that it was greater than we have supposed.

Taking up the problem of the white man's occupation of New
England it is important, in the first place, to remember that the
section was colonized by beef-eating Englishmen. In their native

island, wealth consisted in no small degree in flocks and herds. The immigrants to New England were largely agriculturists, and the number of horses, sheep, and cattle brought by both Pilgrim and Puritan in the first decades of the migration was remarkably large, each ship having from a half dozen to one hundred beasts on board. Allowing for natural increase and for unrecorded importations, we are not surprised to find that a large proportion of colonial laws refer to the herding and branding of cows and to regulations concerning pounds, cow commons, sheep commons, fencing, gates, and bars. The cattle herd at Newton (now Cambridge, Massachusetts) as early as 1635 numbered over one hundred head, and the official cowherd was given two helpers to school it to good manners. The life of the early colonists hung by so slender a thread that they were compelled to take every precaution to conserve wealth.

This is illustrated by the many regulations made by courts and local authorities as to fencing. The "old fields" and newly cleared lands were annually turned over to stock-feeding as soon as the crops were gathered. A large amount of legislation was necessary lest cattle should "damnify the corn and grass," as one regulation phrased it, previous to the throwing open of these protected areas. And among local officers in the colonies, "fence viewers" chosen annually, were far from being of least importance; their value may not inappropriately be compared to that of our fire departments of today. Neglecting to fence one's land was punished severely. Fines for leaving meadow gates open ran from 2s. 6d. upward for each offense, one-half of the amount going to the informer and the remainder to the town; cattle found feeding on meadows "out of season" were impounded, whether attended by keepers or not.

For the purposes of agriculture and herding the comparatively diminutive meadows of New England were necessarily of first importance. What may have been their dimensions in comparison with the rest of the land in early times we have no means of knowing. So far as now surveyed by our Bureau of Soils the meadow acreage of these states today stands: Massachusetts, 41,038 acres; Connecticut, 33,814; New Hampshire, 14,848; Vermont, 3,520;

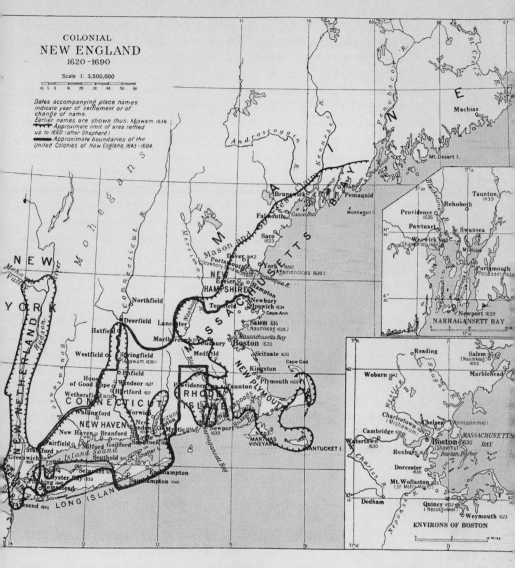

COLONIAL NEW ENGLAND, SHOWING THE ERAS OF OCCUPATION

By permission, from *The Chronicles of America*, published by Yale University Press

Rhode Island, 1,920. Possibly New England as a whole in the pioneer era of occupation (1620–50) could be compared roughly with Berkshire in 1890 when 13,010 acres of abandoned farms were advertised for sale, one-fourth of which were arable. Including meadows entirely or partly cleared, uplands so thinly forested that planting was possible, and grazing lands on the hills, perhaps one-fifth of the land in the pioneer era was of actual use to the colonists.

That these meadows were rich needs no further proof than is afforded by the facts today: acre for acre, Connecticut leads the country in the average number of bushels of corn raised—no state in the famous "corn belt" has equaled its record of forty-one bushels from one acre. The cash value of meadow land as compared with other land in the early times is shown, for instance, in the assessment rates levied in early Hartford; home lots were assessed at forty shillings each, improved upland lots at twenty-five shillings an acre, and meadows in part at forty and in part at fifty shillings an acre.[1] It was never a lack of quality in its good soil that made New England a famous, if deserted, "Mother of Colonies" but rather, the small acreage of good soils. Many other soils influenced New England occupation besides those of the meadow lands; among the chief of these were the Miami, Gloucester, Merrimac, Podunk, Vergennes, Enfield, Elmwood, and Manchester soils, whose crop-bearing values should be mentioned. The Miami series of soils was ever one of the dominating influences in American migration as far westward as the corn belt. The scientific establishment of the name of this soil is a kind of a record of migration, as it superseded Alton, Plainwell, and Edgerton stony loam, Mackinaw gravel, Tazewell silt loam in the East and South, finally finding its name far out in western Ohio. The clay loam of this series, so famous in Ohio and Indiana, is not seen in New England. The silt loam, more rolling and hilly, is less well adapted to general farming, but its yield of wheat is better than that of corn; it produces fruit, especially apples. About five thousand acres of this loam have been surveyed in Rhode Island. The stony sandy loam of the Miami series is represented in New Eng-

[1] W. D. Love, *Colonial History of Hartford*, I, 121, n.

land, seventy thousand acres of it having been so far surveyed in Rhode Island. The stony loam which is good for general farming and apples, and which makes excellent pasturage, is also found in Rhode Island, where 150,000 acres have to the present time been surveyed.

The Gloucester soils are well distributed over New England. The stony loam of this series constitutes a large part of the glacial soils of the region, of which little has been surveyed. Eighty thousand acres have been surveyed in New Hampshire; light yields of corn and potatoes are obtainable on this soil, but in the "chestnut country" in Merrimac County, New Hampshire, it produces excellent hay and pasturage. Rhode Island contains a quantity of Gloucester soil, three hundred thousand acres of which have been surveyed to date. The stony sandy loam of this series gives fair crops of corn, oats, and grass, and good staple crops. In New Hampshire about seventy thousand acres have been surveyed.

The stony loam of the Miami series covers a part of the southern portion of New England; it is found in the Narragansett region, with occasional streaks elsewhere, as in the Blackstone Valley and on the west side of Providence. The excellent pasturage which it provided, together with its fruit-growing qualities, gave to the Narragansett region immediate renown which its fine harbors alone could not have produced. The numerous springs which were found near the coast in Rhode Island, such as the one made famous by Roger Williams, also made those coasts easily occupied. Grazing-grounds, springs, good general farming land and good soil for fruits, especially apples, were a background which must not be overlooked for the development of Rhode Island fisheries, shipbuilding, and commerce.

To that unusual background may also be attributed the greater importance of Rhode Island ports than the Thames River port of New London not far away, although it, too, was a fine harbor and better located because it lay under the lee of Long Island. The "fields of Pawtucket," the Moshassuck region about Providence which, as the name implies, was a famous moose-hunting ground, the Narragansett country where sprang up large landed estates of a type comparatively rare in the North with their flavor of southern aristocracy, and the "great pippin orchard" west of Providence which rivaled the fame of the "yellow sweetings" grown in the Blackstone Valley by the pioneer who gave that valley its name, must all be taken into cognizance with regard to pioneer development along the Sound.

The celebrated tobacco and corn lands in the Connecticut Valley are found on the fine, sandy loam of the Podunk series of soils of which there have been surveyed fifteen thousand acres in the Bay State and two thousand in Connecticut. This strong, safe soil, producing every kind of grain of which the pioneer stood in need, was a main factor in the famous Connecticut Valley migration when Newton, Dorchester, Watertown, and Roxbury people near the coast planted Windsor, Wethersfield, Hartford, and Springfield in the far-off valley.

Of the Podunk silt loam, noted for its excellent grass crops and large yields of hay, New Hampshire has, so far as surveys have been made, one thousand acres, Connecticut about four thousand, and Massachusetts over fifty-five thousand. The character of the soil did not concern the earliest pioneers of New Hampshire, for Portsmouth and Dover (1623) and Hampton (1635) were founded by fishermen. But the story of the settlement of many of the inland towns, as we shall see, is a very different one, particularly of the towns located in the chestnut country about Old Nutfield.

The study of soil survey statistics in the explanation of history gives us a new scientific basis for examining the colonization movement; magnetic forces were strongly felt from regions which bore good crops; the pioneers went by the plain signs of growths, but they were also following accurately, wherever they went, scientific principles unknown to them.

The Pilgrims who landed at Plymouth in 1620 soon found that they had fallen on comparatively sterile land. The cornfields which they planted under Indian tutelage bore crops; yet had it not been for sea food and the corn which was secured from the interior they might have formed another lost colony. Being succored by the maize brought to them from what is now Woodstock, Connecticut, they had the fact very forcibly impressed upon them that a rich Land of Goshen lay somewhere toward the setting sun; but either timidity or the ease of following the line of least resistance, which in them was securing sea food, led them to postpone exploration and expansion toward the fruitful interior. Rather, they clung to the seaboard and sent their sons to Salem, Portsmouth, and Weymouth. The call of the fertile oasis behind them made no marked impression for several years—although as soon as they found that rivals desired it, they were quite ready to dispute its possession.

In the meantime (1630) the Massachusetts Bay Company made its settlements on and about the Bay to the north of the Plymouth colony. Being a much stronger colony and far richer in its flocks and herds, the virility of the Bay Colony soon compelled exploration and expansion such as the Plymouth brethren had not found necessary. The filling in of the shore line and the nearby interior with settlements in the first decade of occupation shows, on the one hand, the growth of New England fisheries, and on the other the call of the inland meadows. The trend of the movement may be measured by the town assessments made by the General Court. Since outlying plantations spread in all directions and advanced faster than formal towns, no exact measurement of their growth is possible; yet it is safe to believe that the inland towns which were most heavily assessed had the largest outlying zones of tributary settlement.[2] In the beginning, it is to be noted, Boston, Dorchester, and Cambridge hold like rank; two of these were interior plantations. Roxbury and Watertown follow, ranking equally, both inland settlements. In a third group, and assessed alike, come Salem, Charlestown, and Lynn. Medford follows; then come Ipswich and Newbury, equally assessed, with Weymouth completing the list. The coast towns, which became so important within a short time, rank well down the list in 1635, with the exception of Boston, the capital of the colony.

The insistent and imperative call of the sea is shown by the figures of 1637, when Salem passes Dorchester, Cambridge, Rox-

[2] For this interesting decade the following table is of value. It is made up from the various scattered references in J. Winthrop's *History of New England*. The amount of assessment, which all had to bear a part in paying, varied in different years; therefore the growth of Boston, for instance, cannot be judged from these

bury, and Watertown, and takes second place in the colony (after Boston). The rise of Ipswich is spectacular, passing every settlement except Salem and Dorchester to the fourth place on the list, while Cambridge falls back. In the year following, Ipswich makes good her position by passing Salem and Dorchester to rank next to Boston, a position not relinquished in the decade.

It was in these years, from 1635–36, that Cambridge, Dorchester, Watertown, and Roxbury were being drained of population to give birth to Springfield, Hartford, Windsor, and Wethersfield, in the Connecticut Valley. The steady rise of Ipswich and the quick regaining of the ground lost by her sister towns shows, on the one hand, that while Ipswich became strong through its growing fleets, the plantations of inland Dorchester, Roxbury, and Cambridge were evidently well located and thriving; at the end of this crucial decade only the three seaports—Ipswich, Charlestown, and Salem—rank above them. The growth of such rural communi-

figures; but, as compared with each other, the relative development of the settlements can be judged roughly from these figures given in pounds sterling:

Towns	1635	1637	1638	1640	1645
Boston	27.6.8	59. 4	57.14. 9	179.	100.
Dorchester	27.6.8	42. 6	36.16. 3	95.	43.17.6
Cambridge	27.6.8	29.12	34.17. 6	100.	45.
Roxbury	20.	30. 8	31.	75.	37.10
Watertown . . .	20.	30. 8	29. 1. 3	90.	41. 5
Charlestown . . .	16.	42. 6	35.13	90.	55.
Lynn	16.	28.16	31.	85.	25.
Medford	10.	24.12	6.15. 8		7.
Ipswich	8.	34.12	46.10	120.	61.10
Newbury	8.	16.18	27. 2. 6	65.	23.
Weymouth . . .	4.	6.16	7.15	21.	10.10
Salem	16.	45.12	44.11. 3	115.	45.
Hingham		8.10	11. 2.10	35.	15.
Braintree				25.	10.10
Colchester				15.	
Dedham				30.	20.
Concord				50.	15.
Rowley					15.
Sudbury					11.5
Salisbury					10.
Hampton					10.
Gloucester					4.17.6
Woburn					7.

ties as Hingham and Concord in this decade is notable, while the
rise of Dedham, Rowley, Sudbury, Braintree, Salisbury, Hampton,
Woburn, and Gloucester show the lines of development in the immediate vicinity of the Bay.

Chapter IX

THE CALL OF THE CONNECTICUT

THROUGHOUT these years, when the "Bay men" were securing their position on the seacoast and the nearby meadow lands, many reports, most of them wholly unrecorded, must have come into the Bay, as well as to Plymouth, of that fertile Land of Goshen across the hills to the westward—the Connecticut Valley. Each large American river valley once made its peculiar appeal, all the way across the continent from the Connecticut to the Colorado and Columbia; and in most cases it was because of the splendid alluvial soils, lying open and ready for occupation. The call of the Connecticut, the reason for the early neglect to answer it, and the compelling causes which led to its seizure are of interest and importance to our theme.

Block, the persistent Dutch navigator from Nieuw Amsterdam, found the Connecticut six years prior to the arrival of the Pilgrims. He named it the "Versche," or Fresh River, because the ocean tides extended such a short distance up the valley. He explored the Connecticut Valley as far north as the Enfield Falls, and trade with the Indians was then inaugurated. "The meadows of the Connecticut Valley," writes a local historian of the Dutch, "were lovely in his eyes, not as the home and inheritance of his race, but for the 10,000 beaver-skins which were annually gathered from thence."[1] Perhaps through fear of Indian hostility which they did not feel strong enough to combat, the Dutch, in 1627, made overtures to the Plymouth men to coöperate with them in Connecticut Valley trade.[2] The invitation was not accepted for reasons no one has clearly defined, but the refusal was probably due to the racial antipathy that persisted despite the Pilgrims' memory of their treatment in the Holland home.

What occurred during the ensuing five years with reference to

[1] H. R. Stiles, *Ancient Windsor*, I, 18.
[2] W. T. Davis (ed.), *Bradford's History*, pp. 223–226.

the Connecticut is a mystery quite as baffling as is the contra-
dictory and inconsistent record of the year 1633. In that year the
Dutch recommended the valley to the Plymouth men as "a fine
place both for plantation and trade."[3] This suggestion was probably made unofficially by those who were ignorant of the purposes
of the Dutch East India Company, which was moving into the
valley to erect the fortified trading station known as the "House
of Gode Hope." This post was built June eighth at Dutch Point,
in the present city limits of Hartford, Connecticut, on the richest
meadow land in the valley.[4]

The Plymouth men referred the Connecticut proposal to the
Massachusetts Bay colony and suggested a coöperative movement.
For reasons as little explained in the records as the real reason for
the Dutch offer to Plymouth and its unenthusiastic reception, the
Bay men declined the overtures made to them. The rulers at the
Bay, it must be remembered, bitterly opposed the first hint of
migration westward from their towns. Good reasons for this existed, but the elemental expansive inclinations of the race could
not long surrender to fear of the aborigines, however closely knit
the fathers might desire to keep the settlements. At an unknown
early date those Daniel Boones of New England, John Oldham
and William Pyncheon, had crept out over the trails which led
into the setting sun across the Worcester hills, and the tales they
brought home had the same effect as those of all our explorers.
To our certain knowledge, Pyncheon made the trip to the Connecticut in 1633. He brought back hemp which was esteemed
better than the best quality grown in England; soil which grew
such excellent crops could not but instantly attract the attention
of men confined to the close quarters in which the Bay settlements
found themselves. Oldham also reported the discovery of lead, a
metal which meant as much to the pioneers as salt did to the
fisheries.

We have no knowledge of the talk which went on or the rumors

[3] W. T. Davis (ed.), *Bradford's History*, p. 299.

[4] Martha K. Genthe, "Valley Towns of Connecticut," *Bulletin of the American
Geographical Society*, XXXIX (1907), 520. This excellent article should be studied
by all who are interested in developing any American river's economic influence on
society, both from the point of view of technique and of subject matter.

that were circulated, but we have good proof that the men of Newton, Dorchester, Roxbury, and Watertown were at once quite alive to the prospect afforded by the rich valley to the westward. The men of Plymouth were also moved, probably by like reports, for Lieut. William Holmes immediately ascended the Connecticut in the wake of the Dutch, and despite their menacing attitude, sailed on by their "House of Gode Hope" and made the first English location in the Connecticut Valley on "Plymouth Meadow" at Windsor, Connecticut. This meadow contained only about seventy-five acres, but adjoining it lay "Great Meadow" containing five hundred acres, and near by, "Sequestered Meadow" of seventy-five acres. While both the Dutch and Plymouth outposts were made primarily in the interests of the fur trade, it was no accident that they were located on the best soil in the valley.

But as is usually true in great migrations, there had to be reasons for leaving an old home, as well as the siren call of a new country, if New England were to project herself into this West. Just how soon it became evident that expansion was necessary to the life of the colony is not sure. That it was keenly felt at Boston as early as the arrival of John Cotton (in 1633) is plain from the fact that in order to keep his people near the church which was given him in Boston, some unusual legislation was necessary. Cotton's followers desired to "sit down where they might keep store of cattle." As he was too good a man to be sent away from the capital city, his parishioners were permitted by law to "take farms in any part of the bay not belonging to other towns." This significantly indicates the crowding that was taking place near Boston.

The more or less unruly herd which belonged to the people of Newton, previously mentioned, may be credited for first seriously upsetting the equanimity of the General Court over this question of migration. When the small size of these river meadows is taken into account, together with the fact that Watertown was not more than a mile and a half distant from Newton, and that Charlestown was not over two miles away, one wonders at the "fundamental error," as Hooker termed it, of locating towns so close together, rather than at the complaint which arose over the cramped condi-

tions. In 1634 the people of Newton filed a formal complaint with
the court; in this they "complained of straitness for want to land,
especially meadow, and desired leave of the court to look out
either for enlargement or removal, which was granted; whereupon
they sent men to see Agawam [Ipswich] and Merimack, and gave
out they would remove, etc."[5]

Reading between these lines, one cannot escape the impression
that the call of the distant valley was far more important than the
brief records that the transaction itself suggests; and this is borne
out in a measure by the fact that men from both Newton, Dorchester, and Watertown now went to the Connecticut on tours of
inspection simultaneously. However, the Merrimac region was also
examined, for Winthrop states: "Being straitened for ground
[Newton] sent some to Merimack to find a fit place to transplant
themselves."[6] No doubt reports of these explorers, as well as those
of others coming by way of Plymouth, as to "the nature and extent
of the [Connecticut] river meadows open to cultivation" incited
activity. At any rate Dorchester men now migrated into the valley
and squatted in an unchristianlike manner on Plymouth Meadow,
evoking Dutch protests which were forwarded by the Plymouth
Company to London.[7] At the same time Watertown men came to
Wethersfield under the leadership of Oldham, and prospectors
from Roxbury spied out the Springfield region under Pyncheon;
the Newton explorers came upon fine meadows near the Dutch at
Hartford. That behind the formal account of this sudden rush
into the valley and the rivalry in finding its best locations there
lies a very human piece of American history, cannot but impress
even the casual reader of Winthrop and Bradford. The one indication of the intimate story of this sudden reaching out of Pilgrim
and Puritan for new lands that remains to us in contemporary
literature suggests in its irony and biting sarcasm a flow of language which might have been exchanged among laymen (out of
their parson's hearing) that would have done credit to any of the
"sooners" of the Ohio or Wyoming valleys in later days.

The details of the Newton migration are better known because

[5] John Winthrop, *History of New England*, I, 157.
[6] H. R. Stiles, *op. cit.*, I, 28.   [7] Winthrop, *op. cit.*, I, 159.

it was the earliest movement of a community or church. The original petition of the people to the Court is extant; it cites specifically the reason for the migration as "their want of accommodation for their cattle, so as they were not able to maintain their ministers, nor could receive any more of their friends to help them." According to Winthrop another reason mentioned was the "fruitfulness and commodiousness of Connecticut."[8] In October, 1635, sixty men, women, and children set out overland from Newton for their chosen plantation where Hartford now is. In the following May, Hooker led the main body of his church over the wilderness trail, driving 160 cattle before them. In these two years all the valley settlements were made and all the rich meadows between Hartford and Springfield occupied. In each case the want of greater room resulted in migration toward fertile land. The case of Suffield, the original southwest corner of the town of Springfield, is an illustration of how dominant were these meadows as determining factors in town growth. This is the only town bordering the river which has no alluvial meadow land; it remained practically a wilderness until the eighteenth century.[9]

These migrations were the first of the long succession which reached at last across the Rockies to the Pacific coast, carrying the seeds of Anglo-Saxon civilization to the farthest West. The story of how each contributed to the momentum of the next would be a new history of our country. For no sooner was Windsor strong and lusty than her men in turn planted Simsbury and Fairfield; no sooner was Wethersfield strong than her men founded Middletown, Newington, Stamford, and Branford; the Indians who sold to the Newton pioneers their land at Hartford departed over their trails to the present site of Farmington, and shortly after, men of Hartford went over the same pathway to found Farmington; and Springfield sent its own waves of migration westward to Westfield or up the valley to Hadley and Northampton and into Vermont. In turn Farmington men founded Waterbury, and the sons of

---

[8] *Ibid.,* p. 167.
[9] M. K. Genthe, "Valley Towns of Connecticut," *Bulletin of the American Geographical Society,* XXXIX, 525, n.

Fairfield and Stamford and Branford could probably be shown to have carried the movement forward into many states.

As in these cases noted, soil for nearly two centuries was a dominant consideration. In the birth of each new frontier the physical conditions were much the same. As the Connecticut frontier was our first American frontier behind the seaboard, it is interesting to notice there the first showing of certain "frontier-isms," which were developed in our history. These are well preserved in the piece of contemporaneous literature mentioned above —Mr. Hooker's famous letter written to answer the critics of Connecticut and the Connecticut migration. The letter clearly shows that the efforts made to thwart migration were wholly based on soil and climate factors. But it is equally interesting because it is the first outcry of an American frontier, the cry of a debtor class to a creditor, of a radical class to a conservative, of a democratic class to an aristocratic. Over and over, as migration continued, the spirit, if not the letter, of this surly, almost recalcitrant challenge from a haughty, democratic, poverty-stricken, but superbly independent pioneer host, was sent back to the critics in the older towns who were the pillars of the churches and banks and legislatures:

Before I express my observations [writes Hooker], I must profess, by way of preface, that what I write are not forged imaginations and superstitions coined out of men's conceits, but that which is reported and cried openly, and carried by sea and land: secondly my aim is not at any person, nor intendment to change any particular, with you; because it is the common trade, that is driven amongst multitudes with you, and with which heads and hearts of passengers come loaded hither, and that with grief and wonderment; and the conclusion which is aimed at from these reproaches and practices is this, that we are a forlorn people, not worthy to be succored with company and no neither with support.

I will particularize. If inquiry be, What be the people of Connecticut? the reply is, Alas, poor rash-headed creatures, they rush themselves into a war with the heathen; and had we not rescued them, at so many hundred charges, they had been utterly undone. In all which you know there is not a true sentence; for we did not rush into the war; and the Lord himself did rescue before friends.

If, after much search made for the settling of the people, and nothing suitably found to their desires but towards Connecticut; if yet then they will needs go from the Bay, go any whither, be any where, choose any place, any patent,—Narragansett, Plymouth,—only go not to Connecticut. We hear and bear.

Immediately after the winter, because there was likelihood multitudes would come over, and lest any should desire to come hither, then there is a lamentable cry raised, that all their cows at Connecticut are dead, and that I had lost nine and only one left, and that was not likely to live (when I never had but eight, and they never did better than last winter.) We hear still and bear.

And lest haply some men should be encouraged to come because of my subsistence or continuance here, then the rumor is noised that I am weary of my station; or, if I did know whither to go, or my people what way to take, we would never abide; whereas such impudent forgery is scant found in hell; for I profess I know not a member in my congregation but sits down well apayd with his portion, and for myself, I have said what now I write, if I were to choose I would be where I am.

But notwithstanding all this the matter is not sure, and there is some fear that some men will come towards Connecticut when ships come over; either some have related the nature of the place, or some friends invited them; and therefore care must be taken, and is by this generation, as soon as any ship arrives, that persons haste presently to board them, and when no occasion is offered or question propounded for Connecticut, then their pity to their countrymen is such that they cannot but speak the truth: Alas, do you think to go to Connecticut? Why, do you long to be undone? If you do not, bless yourself from thense; their upland will ear no corn, their meadows nothing but weeds, and the people are almost all starved. Still we hear and bear.

Chapter X

THE NIPMUCK AND CHESTNUT COUNTRIES

OUR survey has touched on the Plymouth, Massachusetts Bay, and Rhode Island zones of occupation and the waves of migration into the Connecticut Valley. In other zones also factors of soils and growths were equally dominant.

Connecticut had four distinct centers of population—the coast, the river valley above Middletown, the Pomfret-Putnam-Woodstock region, and the Housatonic Valley. While the first settlement of the Sound ports was due to their location on the sea, other influences were also strongly felt. Hydrographic, geological, and soil factors entered into the case. Long Island made the sound in its lee a famous Indian fishing ground. Along this shore, too, were found the northern Indian's "gold mines," as it is not unfitting that we call the noted beds of *pyrula* or *caniculatum,* from the stems or inner whorls of which the best quality of both black and white Indian wampum was made. The thin stream of English migration which crept around on the line of least resistance into sheltered Long Island Sound probably affected even more than the occupation of Massachusetts Bay, the economic status of the red men by cutting them off from their most protected fisheries and from the shores from which their best wampum came. "The manner in which they [the English] improved the land," as an early writer graphically states the case, "and fed their domestick animals . . . must in a short time cut them [the Indians] off from the sea coasts, and quite deprive them of their various fisheries . . . destroy their game in the woods, and in the end quite ruin their hunting."[1]

That the character of the soils determined the extension of settlements to the New Haven region at an early date is established. Israel Stoughton of Roxbury, while tracing the remnants of the Pequots in 1637, wrote the General Court from near New London as follows:

[1] *Massachusetts Historical Collections,* 2d ser., IX, 176.

As for plantation, here is no meadow I see of or hear of near; the upland good, but rocky . . . being, as I judge, stronger land than the bay upland. . . . I confess the place and places whither God's providence carried us, that is, to Quillipeage [Quinnipiac] River, and so beyond to the Dutch, is before [superior to] this, or the bay either, (so far as I can judge) abundantly. . . . It seems to me, God hath much people to bring hither, and the place is too strait, most think. And if so, considering, 1st. the goodness of the land, 2d. the fairness of the title, 3d. the neighborhood of Connecticut, 4th, the good access that may be thereto, wherein it is before [superior to] Connecticut, even in the three forementioned considerations, (for the land Connecticut so judge,)[2] and, 5th, that an ill neighbor may possess it, if a good do not,—I should readily give it my good word [approval] if any good souls have a good liking to it.[3]

Doubtless it was this information which led Davenport and Eaton, founders of New Haven, to make their purchase at the mouth of the Quinnipiac. When they arrived in New England they had been advised to explore the country "beyond Watertown" for a settlement. The conclusion which they reached was:

That, if the upland should answer the meadow ground in goodness and desirableness, (whereof yet there is some ground of doubting,) yet, considering that a boat cannot pass from the bay thither, nearer than eight or ten miles distance . . . we could not see how our dwelling there would be advantageous to these plantations . . . or commodious for our families or for our friends. [An immediate decision being necessary, they sent] letters to Connectacutt for a speedy transacting the purchase of the parts about Quillypieck [New Haven] from the natives, which may pretend title thereto.[4]

It thus becomes plain that questions of soils, as well as ports, were influential in locating the first settlements along the shores of Connecticut.

When the geographical ignorance of the Pilgrim began to be dissipated, he found that it was from the "Nipmuck Country" in Windham County, Connecticut, a comparatively fertile region,

---

[2] This distinction between the inland Connecticut men and those who lived by the Sound is very interesting.

[3] Winthrop, *op. cit.*, I, 479–481.   [4] *Ibid.*, p. 485.

that he had received the corn which had staved off starvation. The numerous lakes of this region also provided the Indians with rank grasses from which they wove mats and thatched their houses; the principal town of the region was Wabbaquasset, or the "mat-producing place." This is modern Woodstock, and through it ran the famous old trail "the Connecticut Path," traversed by Oldham, Pyncheon, Hall, and others in their exploration of the distant valley.[5] This region soon became famous for its "very rich soil" and its "goodly crops of Indian corn."[6] After King Philip's War, Massachusetts purchased this country, and men of the famous Roxbury settlement who had heard of its fertility at first hand (no doubt from John Eliot who labored there among the Indians) at once petitioned the General Court (in 1683) for a tract of land seven miles square at Woodstock and sent a party of pioneers to locate there. "These are the thirteen," begins the old document containing the names of Woodstock's Fathers, "who were sent out to spy out Woodstock as planters and to take actual possession."[7] They found it a rich and "commodiose" place, just as today it is accounted as surpassed in fertility only by portions of the Connecticut Valley.

The same experience was repeated in hundreds of instances throughout New England. One of the most interesting of these was the occupation of the Chestnut Country, where now lie the towns of Chester, Londonderry, and Manchester, New Hampshire, and the projection of the movement through this zone to the present site of Concord. The town of Chester was established in 1720 by "The Society for Settling the Chestnut Country," the first spots settled being Walnut Hill and Hall's Village, famous for their adjoining meadows long known to Indian scouts and hunters. The meadows here were formed through the draining of beaver dams; from this soil sprang excellent grass "which was of great use to the early settler."[8] These meadows lay in all parts of the town, from Three Camp Meadows to the White Hall Mill and Derryfield, now Manchester. The best land lay just below the

[5] C. W. Bowen, *Woodstock*, p. 12.
[6] *Massachusetts Historical Collections*, 1st ser., I, 190.
[7] Bowen, *op. cit.*, p. 22.
[8] Benjamin Chase, *History of Old Chester, New Hampshire*, p. 36.

Congregational church in Auburn and extended to the Londonderry line; to the greatest of these meadows the name Longmeadow was soon applied.

The Chestnut Country was famous for its nut-bearing trees, which, as we have noted, usually indicate good soil. Butternut, chestnut, and walnut trees abounded, and gave the name to the first town on the site of Londonderry, "Nutfield."[9] The founding of Londonderry in this meadow land has peculiar interest because it was peopled by a forlorn company of wanderers who had been buffeted about on land and sea for many months in search of a Promised Land which their leader saw in his mind's eye only. The incident is also of moment because the newcomers forestalled the neighboring Yankees in seizing these meadows and successfully withstood later efforts made to dispossess them.

Early in the eighteenth century a roving Presbyterian clergyman who visited New England, circulated reports of a flattering nature concerning that country in the Ulster district of Ireland. In 1718, 217 Scotch-Irish determined to migrate, and addressed a petition to Governor Shute of Massachusetts stating their "sincere and hearty Inclination to Transport our selves to that very excellent and renowned Plantation upon our obtaining from his Excellency suitable encouragement."[10] This encouragement the Governor offered, and upon their arrival in Boston in the same year the country about Casco Bay was named as fulfilling the requirements of the immigrants. Three hundred of them went there. The Casco country was thoroughly explored but no soil which met their expectations was found. After untold sufferings which included wintering in their icebound ship in the Bay, the leaders of the discouraged company, chief of whom is said to have been James McKeen, grandfather of the first president of Bowdoin College, turned back and ascended the Merrimac. At Haverhill they heard of the Chestnut Country from which men of Haverhill each year brought home splendid crops of hay.[11] In 1722 they founded Londonderry in the Chestnut Country.

What Haverhill men thought of this occupation of their hay-

[9] E. L. Parker, *History of Londonderry*, pp. 313–314.
[10] *Ibid.*, p. 317.   [11] *Ibid.*, p. 137.

fields may be gathered indirectly from the fact that the next summer they proceeded as usual to go up and reap the standing crop. They successfully bluffed off the irate Scotch-Irish who opposed them, but the Presbyterian pastor of the Londonderry flock was not to be thus easily balked. "In very decided though dignified terms," as the local historian puts it, he informed the trespassers that the Scotch-Irish title "to the grass" was "direct and perfect," whereupon the invaders withdrew, but not without insinuating that it was his reverence's "cloth," and not legal title to the meadows, which induced them to pursue this course.

However, the Scotch-Irish were given a "hoist by their own petard" when they in turn, attempted to expand out of their own beaver meadows into the rich intervales of Penacook in the Merrimac Valley where now the city of Concord lies. The first settlement here forms a typical instance of locating a valley town. The alluvial soil of the intervales, a finely grained granitic soil, was well known to hunter, trapper, and ranger for its excellent grass; above, on what westerners would call the "second bench," lay the modified drift soil of the Plains as they were locally known, productive of grains. Beyond lay the upland soils, warm, well supplied with humus, but stony.

The Scotch-Irish were no sooner settled at Londonderry than their outriders found this excellent intervale section of the Merrimac Valley and coveted it. However, Bay State men at Andover, Bradford, and Haverhill, finding themselves "straitened for accommodations for themselves and their posterity," petitioned Governor Shute for these rich intervales, stating that they had "espied a tract of land situate on the river Merrymake (the great river of the said country) whereon they were desirous to make a settlement."[12] How soon the Scotch-Irish got wind of the interest these men took in the "Merrymake" glades we do not know; there is little doubt, however, that their hunters brought word that surveyors had come into the intervales on behalf of the Massachusetts men, for with evident haste the Londonderry men got to the land and built "Irish Fort" (1724) in what is now East Concord.

The surveyors referred to had been appointed by the Massa-

[12] J. O. Lyford (ed.), *History of Concord*, I, 102.

chusetts legislature to mark off the tract applied for by the Bay State men; it is interesting to know that they found it to contain 70,000 acres, only 2,000 of which was "intervale." They reported the inroads of the Londonderry men who claimed to be acting under a New Hampshire grant. The legal phases of the squabble do not interest us beyond emphasizing the desirability of the region and the race to reach it. In January, 1726, the General Court made a grant to a company of one hundred Massachusetts men of a tract of land at "Penny Cook," and that very summer a party of pioneers "made hay upon the tempting intervales on the west side of the river, stacking it for the future use of the 'community.' "[13]

Further illustrations of this process of New England colonization are needless. That there is abundant room here for a rewriting of a good deal of local history is evident when it is realized how incompletely have been analyzed the discovery, rivalry, and occupation of the vast checkerboard of New England meadows and intervales. As each case is examined it is seen that circumstances vary, but the expansive principles remain much the same.

This study is of particular value because it brings home as nothing else can the basic reason that New England was led to develop as it did politically. The New England "town" as a factor in American history is explained by nothing so much as by the New England meadow. These rugged states must be seen in the light of these innumerable spots of vivid green, spots only large enough for a limited number of families in which each one could have an anchorage, so to speak, in fertile meadow lands, but with a larger inheritance of upland, swamp, and forest. The small dimensions of these meadows and the variegated character of adjoining lands, made the raising of a great staple crop impossible; every farm raised every kind of produce which could be grown on the soils represented. In vain did Governor Winthrop open up his "plantation" on the site of the present campus of Tufts College on a scale fitted to the Virginia system, which he copied exactly. New England could not be built that way. No one soil,

[13] *Ibid.*, p. 117.

even in the Connecticut Valley, extended in any direction more than a few rods or miles at the most.

Another very important influence exerted by the diminutive New England meadows, and which extended from them across the entire United States, was the necessity of accurate surveys. Since the meadow was the lifeblood of each New England settlement, every foot of its soil became inordinately precious. When towns were divided into lots, the utmost care was taken in the division of meadow lands; the surveys were carried out to inches and tenths with careful precision. To no feature of town building was more care given than to this; John Doe and Richard Roe knew to a fraction of an inch where their lines of meadow land ran. The deeds which both preserved were deeds as against both the state and their neighbors. The people were trained by necessity to exactness in this particular, and as a consequence knew where all their boundary posts stood, whether in valley or on hill. New England became at once a land carefully marked out, and the moral tone of these exacting requirements wove itself into the substance of their lives.[14]

So far as the writer is aware no one has pointed out fully these influences on the Yankee character. They were undoubtedly present. Being compelled to draw careful lines, to use circumspection with reference to limited meadow lands, to count inches, to guard jealously fences and corner posts, to avoid infraction of others' rights and to protect his own, was doubtless one basic reason for the Yankee's so-called penuriousness, his instinct for saving, his cautiousness, canniness, and "nearness." Nature had been strict with him—canny and "near" and extravagantly exacting. She made him count the inches and the pennies, and her savage winters taught him quickly that he must pay heavy tribute for waste, for prodigality, for slipshod practices, for failure to take the stitch in time.

When this Yankee fared abroad and met, for instance, the

[14] "He [Robert Frost] can smile, as he does in *Mending Wall,* at the peasant-witted farmer who keeps on repeating that 'good fences make good neighbors,' even though the maxim is something he has inherited, not discovered. . . ." Carl Van Doren, "The Soil of the Puritan," *Many Minds,* p. 63.

Virginian on the Ohio or the Mississippi, two distinct types from one ancient ancestry met and looked upon each other, and both wondered marvelously that they could ever have had common forefathers! Comparatively speaking, one was an educated miser and one a gallant spendthrift. One had been bred to go out and get for nothing any tract of land which was not occupied—land richer perhaps than any that New England knew; what did he care for expenses? The other had been bred to the orderly, systematic, methodical township form of expansion under the critical eye of the General Court and the orthodox church. His father or grandfather had been given, let us say, a narrow town lot, with the accompanying right to the common, to a portion of upland and forest. The father of the southerner, on the other hand, probably struck out with his dog and gun into the valley of Virginia or Kentucky and, blazing a tract as big as a New England town, asked the Governor for a patent to it and got it. So different a basis of physical environment could not but stamp itself for generations on the ancestry of each.

Thus the New England township and its government had their basis in the physical necessities of environment. Men paid for what land they got, and knew well just where it lay in longitude and latitude. Other systems developed elsewhere, although their sponsors were no less Englishmen than were the New Englanders, until Webster could say without stretching the truth more than most orators do, that Kentucky was "plastered over" with conflicting claims, although every claimant had a title that was good as against the state. Eighty years ago the Kentucky historian, Collins, found that there were ninety thousand depositions in various land suits in only six of Kentucky's one hundred counties.

In the crisis when a land system for the country at large was to be decided upon, and men seriously inquired into the results of nearly two centuries' experience with the "township" on the one hand, and the "headrights" or squatter system on the other, a committee of Congress composed of more southern men than northern, voted unanimously for the township system of exact surveys which gave title as against both state and neighbor.

The wisdom of this choice has never been disputed; but behind that choice lay the factor of the New England meadow and the imperative necessity which faced Pilgrim and Puritan of giving every holder of a town lot a definitely marked fraction of its soil.[15]

[15] Those land titles were not without their historical importance in many ways. We might never have known the name of the famous *Mayflower* (mentioned by no one of its passengers) but for a land deed which happened to preserve it.

Chapter XI

THE TIDEWATER PIONEERS

BEYOND anything known in New England, the history of Virginia is the history of her soil. For the first century of her existence this story has been splendidly told.[1] The full effect of these influences on the spread of her peoples in the century following, remains to be worked out locally.

The pioneers to the James and York rivers misjudged the numbers of Indian inhabitants because the lower reaches of those rivers contained so many clearings. The Old Dominion was composed of a remarkable aggregation of soils. Those which gave her almost instant fame for her bright leaf tobacco, and which were fitted to grow corn, and finally wheat, were her Norfolk and Portsmouth soils. Already 214,976 acres of Norfolk sandy loam have been surveyed there, as well as 230,272 acres of fine sandy loam of the same series; about 50,000 acres of sandy loam and silt loam each of the Portsmouth series have been surveyed.

This was Virginia's tobacco empire below the Fall Line. In the light-colored sandy Norfolk soils and the dark gray to black surface Portsmouth soils, maize and tobacco thrived wherever the red man girdled or burned the trees which practically covered the land. It has not been shown that tobacco was indigenous here; Jefferson believed it had been imported from South America. But no sooner were the plants in the ground on virgin soil than they developed famously; but they were very exacting, and after three crops, in a land lacking every kind of fertilizing material, the soil began to fail. It was on the Portsmouth soils that were found the enormous strawberry beds which delighted the first comers; and this soil has, by draining and fertilization, become well known in modern times for its truck gardens.

In the Norfolk soils we find the best of Virginia tobacco. The rapidity with which it became sterile gave rise to the many "old

[1] P. A. Bruce, *Economic History of Virginia in the Seventeenth Century.*

fields," which went through three stages, first coming up to rank grass, then being covered with underbrush, and finally showing stands of second-growth timber.

In the first years after the founding of Jamestown the colonists depended largely on grain sent from England and maize obtained from the natives. They made use of the ground about their settlements as best they could, but the virgin soil of the land cleared was too rich for wheat; the nourishment went into the stalk and not into the head. Undoubtedly this fact played a very important part in the development of their agriculture.

What would have happened if John Rolfe had not brought with him to America a smoker's appetite can hardly be imagined. His first experiment to supply himself with the weed was made in 1612; on the result of the experiment, although he little guessed it, seems to have hung the fate of Virginia. The English people were even then expending £200,000 a year for tobacco which came from the West Indies and Trinidad. Maize, the principal crop of Virginia, was unknown to them. And of all exports from the New World, tobacco, of all agricultural products, came nearest to the stern requirement (so ideally fulfilled by the precious metals) of taking up small cargo space in the tiny ships of those days.

Instantly the Virginia colonists took the cue furnished by Rolfe's successful trial, and within three years the destiny of the colony was manifest. This is evident both from the constantly increasing acreage planted and the growth in pounds exported. Our present purpose, however, is best achieved by looking at the matter from another angle—the neglect of diversified agriculture.

England desired that Virginia should become what she needed—a colony producing grain, flax, wine, silk—for which she endured, grudgingly, harsh taxation by her rivals. The Virginians wanted to raise the crop which was financially most remunerative. It took almost a century to fight out the battle. All known methods were tried to make the "tenants" and "farmers" (those who held land in fee simple or on rental) develop general farming. At times it was ordered that each planter should raise a certain number of acres of grain on penalty of forfeiting all of his crop and being reduced to slavery; at times it was obligatory that each land-

holder plant six mulberry trees annually for a series of years. When
parish granaries were established it was required that each male
of eighteen years of age should contribute a bushel of grain a
year; in order that more attention should be given to herds it was
once the law that none should be butchered; and at all times the
number of pounds of tobacco which could be exported to England
was strictly limited.

These efforts are the more interesting because of the fact that
the royal profit on tobacco was enormous, much greater than that
on any other import; but they were steadily pursued until about
1680. By 1614 tobacco had become the staple crop of the colony
—before more than a single plow had been imported. Ralph
Hamor in that year expressed the hope that three or four more
plows would be sent over, since there were then enough steers to
draw them.[2]

Climate and topography were staunch friends of the colonists
in their contest with the home government. The sand and sandy
loams of the tidewater region would have been comparatively
useless in another physical environment. Capt. John Smith was
scientifically correct when he said that "Heaven and earth never
agreed better to frame a place for man's habitation than in Virginia." With a mean temperature between 58° and 61°, amelio-
rated by the warm northwest Atlantic current which mingled with
the Gulf Stream flowing from Florida, and having a liberal amount
of rainfall and a growing season from seven to seven and one-half
months, heaven and earth did well agree.[3]

Topography was also on the side of the adherents of tobacco.
Virginia was an enlarged Venice, so to speak. So remarkably is
it cut up by rivers in the section first occupied which gave to
the colony its economic bent, that plantation life immediately
took firm root. Plantations were governed geographically by the
streams; counties were governed by the plantations; men thought

---

[2] *True Discoveries*, p. 23.

[3] The student of this phase of Virginia's history will enjoy G. T. Surface's studies,
especially in "Climate and Boundaries of Virginia" and "Virginia Trade and Commerce," *Bulletin of the American Geographical Society*, XXXIX (1907), "Physi-
ography of Virginia," *ibid.*, XXXVIII (1906), and "Geography of Virginia," *Bulletin of the Philadelphia Geographic Society*, V (1907).

in terms of plantations and every man was part planter, even though he might be a clergyman, physician, or member of any other profession. The growth of towns and cities was simply not a part of the scheme of society. When late in that first century men bethought themselves of the need of towns, it was too late. "The rural system was so well established," says Professor Bassett, "that it was impossible to overcome its influence."[4] The law of 1691 soon became inoperative because of the objections of the London merchants and the plantation owners, as well as the people at large, who "knew nothing of the advantages of town life and considered the restriction [of trade to designated towns] which sought to bring the trade into the proposed towns a hardship."[5]

Again, the many streams that made it possible for the planter to reach ships with his bright leaf tobacco, rendered road making exceedingly difficult. In 1659 it cost 17.9 per cent of the gross sales to get a ton of tobacco to England. It was an expensive system, but it had come about so naturally that despite its serious handicaps it was already more or less of a fixture. As President Wilson said, in describing Virginia's social conservatism, that colony was more English than England; England changed, but Virginia did not. John Bell Henneman describes this well in his comparison:

The contrast with New England already accentuated by certain differences in people, in attitude, in thought, was here complete. The colonists in Massachusetts and Connecticut, for reasons both natural and social, dwelt in compact communities. . . . Nature and climate and mode of life imposed the one [form of local government] upon New England and the other upon Virginia.[6]

Professor Moses Coit Tyler wrote of the Virginian environment as "constituting a situation out of which may be evolved country gentlemen, loud-lunged and jolly fox-hunters, militia heroes, men of boundless domestic heartiness and social grace, astute and imperious politicians, fiery orators. . . ."[7]

[4] "The Relation between the Virginia Planter and the London Merchant," *Annual Report of the American Historical Association* (1901), I, 553.

[5] *Ibid.*, p. 564; Bruce, *op. cit.*, II, 540–560.

[6] "Historic Elements in Virginia Education," *Virginia Historical Collection*, N.S., XI, 29.

[7] *History of American Literature*, I, 92.

The plantation system, affirms Bruce, "was the result of the special conditions of tobacco culture alone. It did not spring from the existence of slavery, although that institution, by furnishing a cheaper laborer, gave a strong impulse to the expansion of the area included in the tract of each plantation."[8]

Much work remains to be done in analyzing the process of expansion, as anyone will quickly perceive who attempts to ascertain how far up its great rivers "Virginia" extended at the end of the seventeenth century—the period treated by Mr. Bruce. The Fall Line, running southward from Fredericksburg around the head of the Chickahominy to the site of Richmond, was the "frontier" line after the first quarter century of occupation.[9] When it was crossed and by whom, are questions equally mysterious. That the old social order of the tidewater region could not extend itself into a region of unnavigable rivers is evident, unless it had had a training in building roads, a training which was unknown in tidewater "Venetian" Virginia. If the Fall Line was not to be a "dead-line," a new element had to be injected into the situation.[10]

[8] *Op. cit.*, II, 569.   [9] J. E. Cooke, *Virginia*, p. 155.
[10] The relationship of the expansion of plantations to soils and river navigation, and the substitutions for navigation in transportation in the tidewater region, may well be studied with care by local historians.

its right to speculate and profiteer in this Piedmont region. Side by side with the "warlike Christian men" with their muskets and scimitars, with the escaping debtor who found "freedom" in the highlands, and with the hopeful redemptioner and all and sundry "down and outers," strode the land agent of favorites, or even the principals themselves, seeking estates to be engrossed in the same royal way that had been formerly practiced along the lower James and York rivers. Thus the upland became a social mixture. The differentiation in given localities between these types of settlement can well be taken up by students on the ground. The study of such a county as Loudoun would prove interesting from this point of view, occupied as it was by the two civilizations on entirely different soils, one furnishing perhaps as many troops to the Union cause in 1861 as the other furnished to the Confederate.

In general, however, this interior was a democratic "New England" kind of Virginia, and almost from the beginning, down to the woman's suffrage debate of a decade ago, men living on Virginia Cecil and Chester soils have viewed things differently from men living on Norfolk and Portsmouth soils.

On the question of attacking the French beyond the "Endless Mountains," on the problem of fighting the mother country, on the matter of adopting a national constitution, or waging a second war with England, or seceding from the Union, the representatives of these two areas of Virginia held varying views, sometimes diametrically opposed. One may not generalize on such a subject, but attention directed to it locally by competent men will afford material for that "real" history of this nation which will eventually supplant the stereotyped version.

In lowland Virginia the American wilderness operated to transform the English scheme; the English "county" was transferred to it, but it was a different thing in the new environment; men merely called the different thing by the old name. One has but to glance at the outlines of the lowland counties stretching in many cases like giant worms hugging the rivers and occupying the "necks," and compare them with the upland counties, to perceive the geographical influences of the two types of settlements. Above Goochland and Hanover and King William lie the frontier type, such as Fluvanna and Spottsylvania, immediately conforming to the rectangular design which is common to the upland. The two regions had of old been occupied by different Indians, the lowland by the Powhatans and the upland by the Siouans.

Beyond the heads of the Rappahannock lie the Blue Ridge and the famed valley of Virginia. With the occupation of Illinois by the French about 1700, Virginians began to think in a vague way about their own frontier beyond this line of blue mountains. No doubt many hunters had reported on it as mysteriously as was formerly true of the Connecticut in Massachusetts Bay. Lederer and Batts had both conducted exploring expeditions along the old trails into the valleys of the Great Kanawha's tributaries, and in 1716 Governor Spottswood made his celebrated jaunt, nicknamed as an exploration, up the Rappahannock, doubtless crossing the Blue Ridge by the ancient trail through Swift Run Gap. These sporadic expeditions were of no consequence except to keep alive the legends which became current; they arose from no demand on the part of those who should be foremost when actual occupation was undertaken, and who were at this time just entering into their inheritance above the Fall Line.

That valley beyond the blue wall was, however, soon to receive its early adventurous colonizers. But oddly enough they were to come in large part from another colony than Virginia, and in large measure to speak another language than English.

Before turning to survey that movement by way of the back door of Virginia, the Shenandoah, one must question whether this feature of Virginian history has received proper attention. So spectacular was the movement now from the north into the valley that one wonders if the history of the drift from the Piedmont region into that country has not been neglected. Did not many follow Spottswood's trail through Swift Run Gap in these early years of the century? If this is true, it is due the state to establish the facts.

The grant of the Northern Neck, between the Rappahannock and Potomac, was made by Charles II to Thomas Culpepper. The origin of the desire to occupy this region probably antedated 1720. It is greatly to be desired that the movement shall be described

from the Virginian point of view; the origin of the requests for
grants of land here made to Governor Gooch should be studied;
and there should be made clear the purpose and character of
those who precipitated, in the Virginia House of Burgesses in
1729, the question as to whether the Fairfaxes, the Culpepper
heirs, or Virginia, had the right to make grants in the Northern
Neck beyond the Blue Ridge. In that year the Lieutenant Governor stated that he could not refuse to grant land there until the
Fairfax line had been run from the head of the Potomac to the
head of the Rappahannock. Between 1728 and 1733, both the
Governor of Virginia and Lord Fairfax had made numerous grants
in the valley, so many in fact that Lord Fairfax begged the King
to settle the question of his boundary line in order to protect his
grantees.

This dispute between Fairfax and Virginia became an important
factor in the great migration which soon flowed into the valley.
That there is a very important story to be worked out relative
to Virginia's early relations with the lower Shenandoah is evident
to anyone who attempts to differentiate between the racial complexion of this migration and the prior dispositions of the land
so soon to be occupied.

The stereotyped story of the occupation of the valley of Virginia was quite upset by the publication of numerous original
documents by C. E. Kemper in 1905.[1] The first recognized occu-
pant of the valley is believed to have been a German "born at
Shresoin in Germany" by the name of Adam Miller.[2] The date of
his entrance into that region is thought to have been 1726. He was
probably a trader with the Indians who took advantage of a law
passed by the colony in 1705 entitling anyone who established a
trading station "to the westward of or between the Appalachian
Mountains" to hold trade rights for fourteen years.[3] We thus have
an indication that the framers of this law plainly recognized a
fact supposed to have been discovered by Spottswood eleven years

[1] "The Early Westward Movement of Virginia," *Virginia Historical Magazine,*
XII, Nos. 1, 2, 3, and 4.
[2] William and Mary College *Quarterly,* IX (October, 1900), 132.
[3] *Henning's Statutes,* III, 468–469.

later—that the Alleghenies consisted of chains of mountains and were not merely the "blue wall" of Blue Ridge.

There is an important volume of Virginia history latent in the records of this decade from 1720 to 1730. The first official grant to land beyond the Blue Ridge made by Virginia is of itself a conundrum; it is a grant not to land in the nearby valley but to fifty thousand acres far out in the present Bath County on the upper James and Cowpasture, and it was made in 1727. What men knew the rare value of the soils of that region—which was so rich that Virginia chose it not long ago for the site of her state agricultural college? The grant was made to Robert Lewis, William Lynn, Robert Brooke, James Mills, William Lewis, and Beverly Robinson. While this was, no doubt, a pure speculation, the fact that such a superb choice of lands was made by the first men to get a grant from the colony across the Blue Ridge proves how much we have to learn about what men knew of this upland empire.[4]

So, too, our first knowledge of legal proceedings to secure land in the Shenandoah Valley comes in a roundabout way, through the protest of the Fairfax agent, Robert Carter, who objected in 1728 to a grant to Larkin Chew of a ten-thousand-acre patent on "Happy Creek joining on the Great Mountains." We cannot believe that patents were being sought in a region which had not to some degree been thoroughly explored if not occupied. Adam Miller could not have been alone in that wonderful valley garden! No document cited explains where he came from; but judging by what happened in the next decade, it is not difficult to believe that he hailed from the region to the north which was now ready to pour a great stream of migration southward along the line of least resistance and greatest soil attraction.

It is necessary, therefore, for us to turn to Pennsylvania for an explanation for the filling of the valley of Virginia with its important German and Scotch-Irish population.

[4] *Calendar of Virginia State Papers,* I, 214.

Chapter XIII

HUMAN SEED ON STONY GROUND

BEFORE entering upon the story of German and Scotch-Irish occupation of inland and upland Pennsylvania, which forms so interesting an illustration of seed falling on fertile soil, it is informing to review the efforts of groups of those same nationalities to plant themselves elsewhere on our continent. In most cases neither soil nor climate nor environment was favorable to such settlements, and the results were often anything but happy. Soils were factors in these failures; and perhaps only such a *résumé* as follows can prove on the one hand how important they were, and, on the other, how many correlated factors also played their part.

The disciples of the eloquent Jean de Labadie known as "Labadists" came to Bohemia Manor on Chesapeake Bay in 1684. The colony disappeared so completely within the following half century that an ancient map shows the site of a lofty "Labadie poplar" as the only memorial of its former existence. Early in the eighteenth century the German settlements in New Jersey were founded, extending from the Delaware to Hackensack; German Valley and New Germantown were the main towns; these became more or less important villages but did not develop into centers of community life or influence. The story of Kocherthal's colony of Palatinate Germans who in 1708 founded the town of Neuburg on the Hudson (named after the *Stammsitz* of the reigning house of Pfalz-Neuburg in the Palatinate) was a brief one; after a plucky struggle most of the inhabitants went to "Pennsylvania where the German pioneers were in a more flourishing state."[1] The Bernese colony led by de Graffenried to North Carolina landed at the junction of the Neuse and Trent rivers in 1710, where they located their town New Berne named in honor of their Swiss patriots. The savage raids of the Tuscarora Indians, however, scattered the colonists. Some of the refugees came to Virginia and were located

[1] L. F. Bittinger, *The Germans in Colonial Times*, p. 60.

by Governor Spottswood at Germanna on the Rapidan, where they and their descendants formed an interesting colony in the Old Dominion. Others from New Berne drifted to Pennsylvania.

In 1710 upward of three thousand Palatinate Germans came to New York. Governor Hunter placed them on a part of the Livingston Manor; West Camp and Rhinebeck were the towns which they founded. The optimistic governor believed that these immigrants could be set to work making the pitch and tar which were so badly needed by Queen Anne whose *protégés* they were. But their thoughts were for the grapes and grain with which they were familiar, and at the end of a three-year struggle, the Governor ended with the project and told the people to shift for themselves. They had meanwhile heard of the rich Schoharie Valley which was reported as a type of country in which they believed they would feel at home. Explorers were sent forward, and due to their favorable replies the entire colony soon followed, packing all their worldly possessions on their backs. The seed wheat brought with them now yielded eighty-five fold, and but for the manipulations of speculators into whose hands their land fell, the colony might have grown strong. As it was, it broke up. One-third of the settlers moved up into the Mohawk Valley; the rest struck out for Pennsylvania, going along the road to the Susquehanna, and settled finally at Tulpehocken fifteen miles west of Reading.

The fraction of these colonists who chose the Mohawk laid the beginnings of an American Palatinate there of genuine and lasting importance—one of the few which arose outside of William Penn's domain. From Herkimer to German Flats (including Mannheim, Oppenheim, Minden, Palatine Bridge, and Stone Arabia) spread these emigrants and their children. In the Old French and Revolutionary wars they proved their stamina and patriotism; they gave Herkimer, the hero of Oriskany, to the Continental cause, and at Fort Stanwix they raised the American flag for the first time in battle.

In this same era came the first of the waves of Scotch-Irish immigration to this country. Five shiploads of these people arrived in Boston in midsummer, 1718. On July 26 Cotton Mather noted "The many Families arriving [about to arrive] from Ire-

land will afford me many opportunities for kindness to ye In-
digent." Opportunity for kindness came in plenty, but it is more
than evident that New England did not always show Cotton
Mather's charitable spirit. Some day this story will be written
frankly, and, let us hope, by someone with a liberal appreciation
of humor. Two more hard-headed races than the Scotch-Irish and
the Yankee never met and mingled beneath the sun; both had
been bred in a rough school of adversity; both were wedded to
a dogmatic religion and a dogmatic philosophy of life—and they
mixed like oil and water.

We have already noted the fortune of one of the Scotch-Irish
parties which went from Boston to Londonderry, New Hampshire,
in the Chestnut Country. Some of the other expeditions were less
successful. Mather came to Boston's relief (for the problem of
feeding these immigrants was no light one) by suggesting that the
newcomers should find homes in such frontier towns as needed to
be better manned.

Worcester, with its fifty-eight houses and two hundred inhabitants, was such a town. There another colony took its way, one of
whose number at least, had purchased a seventy-five-acre farm
there; this was James McClellan, progenitor of General Mc-
Clellan. "Instead of welcome," writes Mr. Bolton, "they received
surly conversation from the few inhabitants who turned out to
meet them."[2] The colony never prospered. The orthodox citizens
objected, for instance, to the erection of a Presbyterian church,
on the ground that as the "Irish," as they were universally called,
were residents of Worcester they ought to help to maintain the
established church. The feeling reached its climax when the Scotch
began the erection of a sectarian meetinghouse. "The rougher
element," writes Mr. Bolton, "came together one night and destroyed the frame before much progress had been made. . . . It is
said . . . that 'the best people in town' were present."[3]

If such outward show of hostility developed in crises, one can
picture how much infelicity probably accompanied everyday private relations, and it is no wonder that these people for the most

[2] *Scotch-Irish Pioneers*, p. 179.   [3] *Ibid.*, p. 181.

part drifted away to Rutland, to Pelham, and to Palmer; many went to Londonderry where, as an isolated colony, the Scotch-Irish flourished best in New England.

Like the potatoes which one little Scotch-Irish company left, it is said, with some Andover, Massachusetts, neighbors (who in the fulness of time tried to eat the bolls and next year plowed up the tubers and learned their mistake), the seed of this hardy stock grew in after-generations in almost every spot where it was planted in New England. But little could it be imagined, from the small impression made in this orthodox Northland, that the same Scotch stock would yet plant wilderness colonies in America which, because of their indomitable pioneering propensities, their splendid contributions to education, and the growth of democratic institutions, should take front rank in the building of our Republic.

Nor did the Palatinate Germans prosper better in New England than the Scotch. Sebastian Zauberbuhler secured a number of German immigrants to occupy the grant made to General Waldo "on the confines of New England"; they founded the town of Waldoboro, Maine. Waldo himself was of Prussian origin, being a descendant of the von Waldows, a Prussian noble family. Under these influences, also, beginnings of colonies were made at Frankfort, Maine, at "Fort Massachusetts" (Adams County, Massachusetts), and at Braintree, Massachusetts. A petition signed by the wanderers at "Fort Massachusetts" bore the name of Daniel Sachs, great-grandfather of John G. Saxes, the poet. The petition was for a grant of land by the New England system for fields which the forlorn colonists had cleared. A settlement of Germans, led by Joseph Frey from the Bernese Oberland, was made in the eastern foothills of the White Mountains at the present Fryeburg, Maine. From these colonists descended both William Pitt Fessenden (whose ancestor was the village pastor) and the late Senator Frye. But the story of these New England efforts to divert from Pennsylvania a part of the stream of immigration which was making the Keystone State rich is a long one; glass making in Braintree fared no better than tar making on the Hudson; the establishments simply did not take root. A few Germans, some of whom had fought brilliantly at Louisburg for the colonial

cause, remained at Waldoboro. But the story of the Palatinate
German in New England is a story similar to that of the Scotch-
Irish in the same region—unconvincing and colorless.

John Law imported a number of Germans to work in his
"Dutchy" or concession in Louisiana in 1719. They were landed
at New Biloxi and then transferred up the Mississippi to "Ar-
cansas." After the bursting of Law's bubble these unfortunates,
decimated in numbers, attempted to escape from the country.

The bureaucracy recognized their value as pioneers and refused
them passage to Germany; it located them, three hundred in
number, at a point on the river which immediately took the name
Côte d'Allemagne or German Coast. The French Father Du Pois-
son visited them here in 1727: "We slept [he wrote] or rather en-
camped *aux Allemands*. These are the quarters assigned to the
lingering remnant of that company of Germans most of whom
have died of misery, some at the east [Dauphin's Island] and
some on arriving in Louisiana. Great poverty is visible in their
dwellings."[4]

Perhaps no more forlorn colony came to America than this.
But in their final home they found rich soils to their liking, and
their thrift and willingness to work before long brought its reward.
They turned the *Côte d'Allemagne* into *Côte d'Or*, the "Gold
Coast," and from them, according to the Louisiana historian,
Gayarre, "have sprung some of the most respectable citizens of
Louisiana and some of the wealthiest sugar planters of the State."[5]

A former director of John Law's "Compagnie des Indes," Jean
Pierre Purry of Neufchatel, Switzerland, conceived the idea that
countries which were under the influence of the sun at the exact
angle of thirty-three degrees of latitude were particularly favored.
He promoted a colony of Germans on the Savannah River; it
founded Purysburg, South Carolina, but was short-lived.

South Carolina, however, became a successful field for exploitation by the Palatinate Germans. Orangeburg County in that
state has given its name to a famous soil—the best general farm-

4 *Early Jesuit Missions*, II, 236, 262–266, 267.
5 *Louisiana*, pp. 360–361.

ing land, perhaps, in the whole South. It is useful, writes Mr. Whitney, "for truck, fruit, and the staples corn and cotton."[6]

Curious evidence exists that the promoters of South Carolina land schemes used questionable tactics in attempting to divert from Pennsylvania the tide of migration. For instance reports that the Penns had quarreled with the Palatinate Germans were circulated, as were rumors that Penn had ousted some because of their religion.[7] From an inconsiderable beginning in about 1731, the Palatinate German migration to South Carolina became extensive within four years. The trail upcountry from Charleston was followed, and Orangeburg was occupied and named in honor of the Prince of Orange. Numerous other settlements were made in Chesterfield, Newberry, and Lancaster counties. This Palatinate German population in part drifted northward with the years, into the mountains and beyond, in every direction. Many of these immigrants were redemptioners; upon receiving freedom they became, as was true of their counterparts in Virginia, very valuable frontiersmen and settlers.

The Orangeburg settlement was famous as the original scene of the labors of John Witherspoon; with a colony of some twenty-five other heads of families, this giant among men arrived in South Carolina in 1734. Radiating from Williamsburg many offshoots of the original colony were sent out to establish inland settlements at Indian Town, at Salem, at Mount Zion, and at Brewington.

South Carolina well illustrates the decided capacity of these people for wilderness mastery. The lowland settlements languished as the upland progressed. The German was not fated to succeed in a typical southern plantation environment; while at the same time, far up between the Broad and the Saluda, at Spartansburg, in the Waxhaw country, and in the table-lands of the Watauga and Tennessee, where farming on the individual scale offered free play to the spirit of initiative and independence, as we shall see he came into his own.

Why this could not have happened in New England is explained partly by the difference between the southern and northern land

6 *Soils of the United States*, p. 107.   7 Bittinger, *op. cit.*, p. 123.

systems, partly by Indian opposition (although this was felt also
in the South), and partly by the "feel in the air," that indefinite
influence produced by a sense of relationship, or of the lack of it,
established between an individual and his environment.

Despite the fate of Purysburg, Governor Oglethorpe of Georgia,
the William Penn of the South, encouraged the migration of many
Salzburgers from their homes in the Tyrolean Alps to his colony.
By 1740 there were over twelve hundred Salzburgers, Swiss, and
Pfalzers in Savannah. The success of the enterprise led to further
migrations as well as to the founding of interior plantations.
Through upland Georgia went many hundreds of pioneers, former
redemptioners, to swell the inland population of Lutheran sects.

The importance of the success of the Germans in establishing
themselves firmly in Georgia and the Carolinas was manifest, as
we shall see; for, beyond the mountain barriers, delightful valleys,
rich and fertile, were found fit for general agriculture where poor
men might reign as kings.

At a very early day Port Royal and Charleston contained Scots
—both freemen and prisoners captured in battle and deported.
Two clergymen had served an independent church, sometimes
called a Presbyterian church, in Charleston between 1685 and
1720. In 1732 men seceding from this original organization formed
a new church because the old seemed to them tainted too greatly
with Congregationalism.

Meager data relating to these organizations are all we have
that proclaim the beginnings of Scotch-Irish migration to Port
Royal and Charleston, and the establishment of an influence in
both lowland and upland South Carolina which would later prove
of great educational and political value. The migration increased
considerably, it is believed, in 1719, when lands abandoned by
the retreat of the Yamassee Indians were thrown open to Protes-
tant adventurers who were granted two hundred acres each on
the Island of Port Royal. Thus Beaufort, and later the township
of Williamsburg, were occupied in large part by the Scotch.

Chapter XIV

PENN'S FOREST EMPIRE

IT would have been difficult to foresee, from the German experiments in various parts of the American colonies, that one of the world's most famous agricultural developments would evolve in what came to be known as Pennsylvania.

The first three shiploads of William Penn's emigrants to the forest empire which King Charles named "Pennsylvania" arrived at the future site of Philadelphia in 1681. Before Penn himself came in the year following, he had widely circulated advertisements of his grant.

It is certain that Penn had received very fair reports concerning his lands, evidently from Swedes or Dutchmen to whom the Delaware and Schuylkill had been familiar for many years, and there is a poise in his descriptions of the country which signifies clearly his reliability. Writing to the Committee of the Free Society of Traders in 1683 he said:

The country itself, its soil, air, water, seasons and produce, both natural and artificial, is not to be despised. The land containeth divers sorts of earth, as, sand, yellow and black, poor and rich: also gravel, both loamy and dusty; and in some places, a fast fat earth; like our best vales in *England*; especially by inland brooks and rivers: God, in His wisdom, having ordered it so, that the advantages of the country are divided; the back lands being generally three to one richer than those that lie by navigable rivers. We have much of another soil; that is a black *hazel-mould,* upon a stony, or rocky bottom.[1]

It is significant that the proprietor should have emphasized in this, perhaps his earliest, description of Pennsylvania that most

[1] Quoted by R. Proud, *The History of Pennsylvania,* I, 247. The richest lands in Penn's grant were not black soils, whether he thought so or not. It is possible that he was deceived by the black soil in the Conowingo, or Serpentine "barrens"; seldom, if ever, is black soil so unfertile as this, due to the quantity of magnesia present in it. F. W. Pennell, "Flora of the Conowingo Barrens," *Proceedings of the Academy of Natural Sciences of Philadelphia* (1910), p. 543.

unique characteristic—the fertility of those uplands "by inland brooks." No similar report had ever been sent back from the New World to the Old; for the lands mostly heard of in America had always been reported from valleys—from the Connecticut, Hudson, Delaware, Potomac, James, and Savannah. In describing the crops to be grown most successfully on Penn's lands, wheat takes precedence; whereas in all other similar reports from America corn or tobacco had taken precedence. The other grains Penn describes are barley, oats, and rye; corn and tobacco are not mentioned.[2]

We shall soon see that Penn's lands were more valuable than he suspected, but it is important first to emphasize his method of handling and disposing of the land. We have noted the two systems employed in the North and in the South; New England with its pioneers making compact settlements (moving out to their specific haven under the close scrutiny of Court and Church) and Virginia dominated by its engrossed estates and headright proprietors.

Penn chose the Dutch "patroon concessions" scheme as his main plan of land selling, but the variations he adopted brought about an anomalous situation. Penn and his sons divided the land into three parts called common lands, proprietary tenths or manors, and the private estates of the individual proprietors. Each share or proprietary was to consist of a five-thousand-acre tract or "head stem," as the Frankfort Company which founded Germantown called it. The price of these shares was one hundred pounds, with a quitrent of a shilling per annum per one hundred acres.[3] Estates as small as two hundred acres were, however, rentable by paying a quitrent of a penny an acre; all who took five hundred acres also received a Philadelphia ten-acre lot. Thus while the Welsh Tract, for instance, ran from the Schuylkill to Darby Creek, and embraced sixty-two and a half square miles, it was also possible for a pioneer to secure a diminutive farm.[4]

[2] Proud, *op. cit.*, I, 250.

[3] W. R. Sheppard, "The Land System of Provincial Pennsylvania," *Report of the American Historical Association* (1895), pp. 117–118; also, C. H. Browning, *The Welsh Settlement of Pennsylvania*, p. 33.

[4] "Article of Agreement Between the Members of the Frankfort County," *Pennsylvania Magazine of History*, XV, 205.

We see, therefore, that Penn combined both the northern and the southern systems and encouraged both compact settlement and individual enterprise. Unfortunately the scheme made possible a vast amount of illegal squatting, for in a large number of cases lands were granted to those who never saw or expected to see them. The unbusinesslike way in which the matter was handled also made matters worse, and led to other difficulties.

To the first Dutch and Swedes who came into the country where Philadelphia was laid out, the section was known as "Upland" in contradistinction to the occupied regions lower down on the Delaware. When Chester County was first named it was called "Chester alias Upland"; it contained at the time of Penn's arrival about five hundred Dutch, Swedes, and Welsh. Quaker meetings were held in "Upland" as early as 1675. It was undoubtedly from these pioneers that Penn received his information about his fortunate inheritance, but it is desirable that every source should be examined in the hope that more light may be thrown on the exploring done by these traders which made possible the securing of such information as Penn possessed.

The empire which Penn acquired was admirably fitted for occupation by an industrious people. Here as in New England and New York the enterprises of the Dutch had been confined to Indian barter, although never a land held out finer prospects to the home builder, whatever his nationality—and Pennsylvania received all comers into its fertile lands.

We have noted the advantageous position of Philadelphia. A proper understanding of the sudden rise of Pennsylvania can only be gained by viewing its eastern zone through the geologist's eyes. This fertile Paleozoic region is divided into several belts of rock and soil and the sequence of four of these should be seen from the point of view of their relationship to Philadelphia, the center and ocean port from which radiated the inland movement.

A glance at the map shows, first, that northwest from that city a band of sandstone (gneiss) runs from the northeast to the southwest and is bisected by the Schuylkill River. Splitting this belt, two long prongs of primal sandstone come up from York County, while near the center of Chester County lie some little islands of limestone soil on which the Quakers planted one of their offshoot settlements (Kennet) as early as 1707.

Secondly, we see that this sandstone belt is divided by a long, curious limestone valley running from Willowgrove in Montgomery County to the eastern fringe of Lancaster County. The main line of the Pennsylvania Railway System runs straight from Philadelphia to this thin strip of limestone at Paoli, whence the line turns and follows it to the limestone oasis of Lancaster County beyond—the goal of early migration and the richest county, agriculturally, in the United States. The converging of the various lines of communication in this rich valley, in which Downington and Coatesville lie, indicates its strategic character. The Conshohocken Hills marked the limit of Penn's first grant of land from the Indians (1683); but in two years he was ceded all of central and western Montgomery County to which the Schuylkill led, and migration following the river northward at first missed entirely the rich limestone region.

North of Chester, on the highlands of Skippach Creek beyond the Conshohocken Hills, was planted one of the early inland German settlements antedated only by a settlement in the narrow limestone vein north of Germantown.

Thirdly, to the west of Chester County lay the marvelous but half-hidden limestone zone of Lancaster County, drained by its Conestoga Creek—known in the history of American transportation because of its horses and its wagons. On the north of it, the red sandstone of Montgomery County swings around southward hemming the limestone region in to a mere finger tip south of the Susquehanna, where the primal sandstone region of York County comes westward to meet it. Yet in that finger tip, where lie the flourishing towns of York and Hanover, is the far-famed valley of Pennsylvania.

Fourthly, we see in the west, beyond the wide sandstone belt marked by Gettysburg and South Mountain, a broader limestone valley which comes circling all the way around from Easton on the Delaware; its fertility has made the towns of Bethlehem, Allentown, Reading, Carlisle, Shippensburg, and Chambersburg what they are. This is the Appalachian Valley, a noted avenue lead-

ing to the Potomac by way of Hagerstown, Maryland. Its rich soil
has been officially given the name of that town, "Hagerstown."

It is only by getting a working knowledge of these four divisions
of soil that one can appreciate in detail the inspiring story of the
occupation of Pennsylvania. But the tale cannot be inspiring so
long as the names of towns and streams and counties are merely
geographical figures of speech; there is an insistent and far-
reaching meaning to them, a most interesting background behind
them; it is by appreciating this fully that the unfolding drama of
occupation can become vital. It is the difference, as we have remarked before, between knowing a man and knowing both a man
and his ancestry.

Other controlling influences beside the physiographic were always present when the unprecedented rush of Palatinate Germans,
Swiss, Scotch-Irish, Irish, Welsh, and English suddenly flooded
these hills and vales with their pioneers; one of these was Indian
relations; and yet the flush tide of 1700 to 1730 swept across this
land and the lust of land-hungry men for the garden spots marked
by Lancaster County and the great limestone Appalachian Valley
beyond South Mountain, was not to be denied.

With the arrival of Penn's efficient agent, Pastorius, and the
successful planting of Germantown in 1683, the movement to
occupy the Pennsylvania interior may be said to have begun; for
it was colonists of this type rather than the Quaker who should
make famous these fertile soils. In every sense it was the Palatinate Germans' natural environment, resembling closely the country from which they hailed both in soil and climate.[5]

Thirteen of the Mennonites and their families led by Pastorius
from Holland founded the town of Germantown on the highlands
east of the Schuylkill in 1683. The prosperity of the settlement
was instant, in remarkable contrast to the record of the first year's
experiences of the English at Plymouth, Boston, and Jamestown.
Several factors explain this; not the least of these was the satis-
faction felt over the crops raised by these emigrants from Hol-

[5] Doubtless an antiquarian could find hundreds of instances in our history of
Europeans being influenced in their choice of seats in the United States by home-
land predilections. Cf. "Why Hollanders Came to Iowa [instead of to Michigan],"
Iowa Journal of History and Politics, IX, 531.

land the first year. One of them wrote to friends in the homeland
the first year after migrating: "I have so much grain, such as
Indian corn and buckwheat, that this winter I shall be better off
than I was last year."

With the Conshohocken Hills barrier removed by Penn's second
treaty with the Indians, the Whitemarsh region of Montgomery
County was occupied—within five years after Penn's arrival.
Within fifteen years (in 1702) the Shippach highlands to the
north boasted a Mennonite settlement; and by 1740 all the lands
of Montgomery County were parceled out.[6] Swedes, Welsh, and
English predominated in the south and center, Germans in the
northwest, and Dutch, French, and Scotch-Irish from the center
eastward to the Delaware.

The acquaintanceship between the Mennonites who settled
Germantown and their brethren in Switzerland in the old days
of persecution in Europe had been very close; frequently each had
protested against persecutions which had been directed at the
other. It was most natural, therefore, that those who came to the
New World should report to their forlorn Swiss friends concerning
the prosperity which was theirs in Pennsylvania. These reports
from Germantown were not without avail, embellished as they no
doubt were by the representations of Penn agents in Europe; and
they gave rise to one of the most unique migrations in American
history, judged by its results.

The leading spirits in this movement were Hans Herr and
Martin Kendig; these with eight others secured a warrant for ten
thousand acres in the interior. It is greatly to be hoped that new
light can some day be thrown on the reason for the site chosen
for their land in this year of 1709. No settlements had been yet
made even in what is now the western part of Chester County.
Yet with a prescience, concerning which we could wish to know
more, they chose land on the north side of Pequae Creek, far out
in what is now Lancaster County, as the site for their settlement
—the first to be made in that future garden spot of the eastern
portion of the United States. The price paid, five hundred pounds,
was, however, about double the regular price Penn had set for

[6] T. W. Bean, *History of Montgomery County*, p. 104.

other lands. Yet it was the best land bargain ever made in colonial times.[7]

These Lancaster County pioneers included the agents named, and also Hans and Martin Meylin, John Herr, John Rudolph Bundely, Jacob Miller, Martin Oborholtz, Hans Funk, and Wendel Bowman. The splendid site they chose had long been the home of the Conestoga Indians, named from Conestoga Creek, the principal stream of this region, which lies west of the Pequae. To all this zone the Susquehanna was the key and the Conestoga and Pequae were its tributaries. Through this avenue Indian traders of various nationalities had been active for half a century. From some of these Herr and Kendig must have received their information. The earliest descriptions of Lancaster show these grassy uplands to have been quite treeless: "These flats of Pequae [wrote Redmond Conyngham] were natural meadows on which grass grew luxuriantly, which proved a great source of comfort to the new settlers."[8]

We have noted that hickory trees betokened good land. It so happened that a hickory tree, standing beside a spring here in these grassy fields, was the spot chosen as the site of this colony's settlement and they named it, in honor of the tree, Hickory Town; the name was later changed to Lancaster.

The news of the planting of a colony in the domain of the Conestogas spread rapidly. The colonists of Hickory Town at once remembered relatives and friends living in Switzerland under conditions incomparably inferior to their own, and they soon sent their agent and pastor, Hans Herr, back to the old home to tell the story of this veritable Land of Goshen beside the silvery Pequae. Numerous "head stems" were secured in this country in the following years. The order in which these were secured, and the nationalities represented, need to be worked out by students in close touch with the original records. Many small grants were taken out, such as Martin Kendig's for two thousand acres in 1712. By 1726 it was stated that 100,000 Dutch, Irish, Scotch-

[7] For purposes of comparison it is interesting to know that at about this time (1718) Gershom Rice of Worcester, Massachusetts, was selling James McClellan, the Scotch-Irishman, seventy-five acres for £41. (Bolton, *op. cit.*, p. 179.)

[8] Quoted by I. D. Rupp, *History of Lancaster County*, p. 112, n.

Irish, German, Welsh, and English settlers had squatted "without a shadow of right" in Penn's forest empire! Whatever the facts were, this limestone zone of Lancaster County soon had its full proportion of legal purchasers, renters, and squatters.

Between fifteen and twenty thousand Germans came into Pennsylvania before 1727. We have seen that both the Germantown and Lancaster pioneers were eager to let their countrymen know of their pleasant lot. Doubtless there has been exaggeration as to American migrations from Europe due to European wars. Probably careful study would show that it was such communications as those now sent from Germantown and Hickory Town, in connection with the evident activities of speculators, that were the more potent agencies of migration. The large Scotch-Irish immigration of this same period did not come from a war-ridden country but from an economically oppressed country. The fear of war, the increased taxes demanded by the electors of the Palatinate and adjacent countries, and the glowing accounts of Pennsylvania seem to have dominated the German migration; but the reports of the first comers doubtless, after all, exerted the greatest influence.

Steadily through these decades from 1710 to 1730 immigration poured in from every direction, focusing on Lancaster. The wanderers from the Schoharie, whose fortunes we have noted, came down the Susquehanna from the North with Conrad Weiser and settled at Tulpehocken near Womelsdorf. Famous men of the border came in, whom Conrad Weiser was one day to serve in most responsible positions, men like John Wright, who settled at Columbia, and Le Tort and Chartier, who came to the Susquehanna. The Dunkards made their first settlement in the rich Ephrata region; fertile Oley was occupied, and also Falkner's Swamp. By hit and by miss, choice bits of land were found and pounced upon, as when Hans Graaf found rich land while pursuing stray horses at the head of Grove's Run. On the other hand great tracts, some of which were purchased much more cheaply than others, were allocated to speculators. The owners of the "London Lands" for instance, holding nearly fifty thousand acres in Lancaster and Berks counties, valued them in 1720 at £2 per hundred acres rental; while Thomas Penn estimated his thirteen-thousand-acre "Conestoga Manor" worth £40 per hundred acres.[9] And everywhere in Montgomery, Lancaster, Berks, Northampton, Dauphin, Lehigh, Lebanon, Monroe, Center, Adams, and Cumberland counties, squatters of almost as many nationalities spread.

Phenomenal prosperity was reported in many cases; Lancaster had not been settled a generation when Andrew Ferree, who came with no worldly goods worth the mention, estimated his farm tools and chattels alone to be valued at over £150. Wheat, which we have seen could not be grown successfully at first on the soil of tidewater Virginia, brought a return of from twenty to thirty bushels an acre here the first year; forty-five grains of corn on a single ear, seventy ears of rye on one root, forty-five of wheat, eighty of oats and from ten to fourteen of barley—such were the reports which broadcast the fame of the first granary of America.[10]

Germans predominated in the richest counties of eastern Pennsylvania; in 1789 Benjamin Rush named the most fruitful centers of the state as Strasburg and Mannheim in Lancaster, Lebanon in Dauphin, and Bethlehem in Northampton.[11] This was due in part to the instinct of the Palatinate German for handling this kind of soil. For thirty centuries their ancestors had cultivated one of the richest wheat-growing regions of Europe;[12] every necessary tool, every trick of the trade, every knack in the art, was a latent accomplishment in the tradition of these people and even their experience in using irrigation in European fields and vineyards was of value to them in Lancaster County.[13]

Many lines of development were corollary to this great agricultural development. But it is for us here to observe the fact that in a favorable environment the Palatinate German created America's first and richest granary. Recalling now the failures of so many German colonies in this country, we have it impressed upon us that while governmental agencies contributed largely to make famous this episode of migration, the factors of soil, climate,

[9] J. Sparks, *Writings of Franklin*, II, 553.
[10] Browning, *op. cit.*, p. 40.
[11] *Manners of the German Inhabitants of Pennsylvania*, p. 55.
[12] Proud, *op. cit.*, I, 274.
[13] *Pennsylvania Magazine of History*, XVIII, 215.

and vegetation were present to exert a significant influence. Other governors had striven to parallel Penn's hospitality; but they did not have behind them those thousands of acres of Hagerstown limestone soil. In this success in developing just the region suited to their knowledge and culture these first Pennsylvanians exhibited one of the most interesting cases in history of the reaction of man to soil. In their passion for limestone soil they measurably kept out rival races; other factors entered into this, of course, particularly the poverty of would-be competitors; but a vital factor was the prosperity of the Germans.

Yet Pennsylvania was the melting pot of America in these booming years of the eighteenth century. We cannot attend to the ramifications and propensities of each claimant to attention; but to one of these groups, the immigrants from Scotland and Ireland, we must devote liberal space.

Chapter XV

SCOT AND CELT ON THE AMERICAN
FRONTIER

COLUMBUS' first ship brought from Europe to the West Indies, it is said, two Irishmen as members of its crew. From the earliest days the Scot and the Celt have played an important part in the development of our nation; on the farm of a Scotchman was fought the final battle to decide whether England or France should dominate this continent—the "Heights of Abraham" Martin. From Canada to Georgia, as we have seen, a sprinkling of Scotch, Irish, and Scotch-Irish might have been found in every colony as the years went by. Wherever there was work to be done the Celt was found, but always in the rôle of a freeman or a prospective freeman. His greatest contribution to the physical conquest of the continent was made in the nineteenth century, but it was in the rôle of Indian trader and pioneer on all our frontiers that his nonchalance in the face of danger, his cunning and imperturbable good nature, made the Irishman's service more significant than has been recognized.

To the peace-loving Quaker and Mennonite, the irrepressible Irish and dogged Scotch formed a much-prized obstruction to screen them from the red man. Just as the acacia puts out ant food on the ends of its leaflets which induces those insects to guard it from the ravages of death-dealing parasites, so all who were concerned in selling or settling the rich wheat lands in Penn's forest empire were generous both in granting frontier acres to each of these land-hungry races, and in winking at squatters— provided these were between them and danger! How utilitarian were the motives which prompted this generosity the squatters often found out soon; for with the passing of danger, they frequently discovered that their claims to the lands they had occupied were not based on sound title. In numerous cases they were told without compunction to pay up or move on. Instead of being

a "thin red line of 'eroes" they suddenly found that they were
proscribed and anathematized. Yet in that marvelous half century
between 1700 and 1750 they did heroes' work even if they received
in the end what was far from hero worship.

It is plain how the wheat-bearing region of Pennsylvania should
have become a noted horse-breeding region. The stocky Conestoga
horse arose out of that grain-producing country just as naturally
as, later, the McCormick reaper first appeared in it. What with
importations, and the crossing of the English hunter with the
Indian pony which came up from the Apaloose country east of
New Orleans, the breeding of horses in the Philadelphia region
was a business even in the year of Penn's arrival. Penn then wrote
(1683): "We have no want of horses; and some are very good
and shapely enough; two ships have been freighted to *Barbadoes*
with horses and pipe-staves since my coming in. Here is also
plenty of cow-cattle, and some sheep; the people plow mostly
with oxen."[1]

From his description it is evident that he was judging by English standards and was writing of more or less native stock. The
place which the cattle-raising industry occupied from the very
first is indicated by the following remark of one of the first immigrants: "To be a peasant and nothing else is a sort of cattle-
life."[2]

These facts explain why the pack-horse trade with the Indians
became of greater importance in Pennsylvania at an earlier day
than in any other colony. For this trade the Irish showed a natural
leaning, as did also the Scotch-Irish; and although many Germans, like Weiser, entered into it, there is doubtless room for the
assertion that the Celtic stocks took more naturally to it, though a
lack of capital must also explain this in part.

Comparisons like this are, however, of no great significance;
the vital fact is that the country was the natural environment for
the development of the pack-horse trade and that it was followed
by all nationalities. Sturdy beasts were raised here fit for the

[1] Proud, *op. cit.*, I, 251.
[2] Oscar Kuhns, *The German and Swiss Settlements of Colonial Pennsylvania*,
p. 43.

journey over the "roads of iron" through Kittanning Gorge or over the highland pathway through Bedford to the Ohio Country where, as early as 1749, the French found them and sought to undermine their trade.

In this work of exploration—for be it understood that every such trader was also an explorer—the Irish and Scotch-Irish were famous, as has been made clear by their annalist, Charles A. Hanna.[3] These traders found the landward routes to the West; they learned the characteristics of the Indian tribes with whom they did business, and came to know which were easy to conciliate and which were difficult; they first understood the ups and downs of Indian allegiances, the chieftains who were to be trusted and others who were not. They learned to know which land was good and desirable, which was inferior, and what routes to each were preferable at every season of the year; they knew where the rivers lay that were to be feared, and how and where the best crossings could be negotiated. In the end they became the guides and trusted confidants and treaty makers of generals of armies; and they became the mentors of all who were seeking new lands. This wider service of the "Indian trader" has not had its historian; as a man familiar with the whole frontier he played his most important rôle in empire building, and his record as such deserves intensive study in the field to which Hanna has paved such a broad highway.

The most vital factor in this Indian trade, as well as in the trade with the whole fast-filling frontier, was preëminently a German contribution and has never been properly emphasized except in the works of specialists. It was firearm manufacture, and repair and ironwork of a similar character. It will be remembered that the Meylins were among the first of the Mennonites to settle near the Pequae; these were the first gunsmiths on our frontier— an occupation which, more than any other, was the need of the hour in the wilderness. The Deckard rifle was a Pennsylvania product and along with horseshoes and wagon tires, became one of the chief tools in the conquest of the West.

The story of the Scotch-Irish immigration from the north of

[3] *The Scotch-Irish, The Wilderness Trail*, etc.

Ireland to America resembles in numerous respects that of the
Palatinate Germans which we have described. While not so commonly agriculturists as the Germans, and entering more frequently
into the many lines of business which opened a way to earn a
livelihood in towns and cities, the bulk of this hardy and prolific
"seed" (which meant so much to America from the religious,
educational, and political points of view) sent down its first roots
in appropriate soils. The records of the migration, which began
approximately at the same time as that of the Palatinate, seem to
show first that it was not promoted so much by land agents, and
second, that the Scots, however poor, maintained a rugged passion
for independence, even if they had first to gain capital and experience by serving time as redemptioners.

This craving for independence made them admirable frontiersmen; but they excelled in the work they had to do in an environment to their liking. We have glimpsed one colony of them, the
dogged invaders of the beaver meadows of the Chestnut Country
in New Hampshire. Of the numerous attempts to establish themselves in New England, only the one made at Londonderry was
a marked success, and that, of course, was on a very small scale
so far as numbers were concerned. The antipathy of the Yankees
toward them is illustrated by the Yankee author of a recent volume who devotes two hundred and sixty-five pages to the reasons
for their migration and to their insignificant history in New England, and only forty-seven pages to their great and colorful record in the other colonies! A local study should be made of the
reactions of the two sturdy stocks upon each other in New England at Boston, Londonderry, Worcester, where a mob among
whom were the "best people in town" burned, as we have seen,
the frame of the Scotch-Irish church.[4] Local studies of their activities in Ware, Windham, Antrim, Peterborough, Colerain, Bland-
ford, Palmer, and elsewhere might be undertaken to advantage.
That other things besides theological differences were serious
barriers to amicability is shown by Benjamin Chase who, in conformity to local custom, refers to the newcomers invariably as
"Irish": "The Irish ate potatoes and the English did not; the

[4] *Carl's Tour in Main Street* (Worcester), VIII, 146.

Irish churned their milk and drank buttermilk and the English did not; the Irish put barley into their pot-liquor and made barley broth, the English put in beans and had bean porridge."[5]

When such fundamental differences as these existed, what wonder that Yankees felt that "intermarriages were considered improper," and that "as late as 1762, when Benjamin Melvin married Mehitable Bradley, it was considered an improper relation!"[6]

The best environment for potatoes, buttermilk, and barley lay to the south of New England; and soon through Newcastle and Philadelphia streamed hundreds and then thousands of the Celts. While no special thought was given to the order of their coming, and while most of the counties in the fertile background of Pennsylvania received a part of this excellent strain, the old clannish loyalty held definite sway and the lines of least resistance were, first to regions already occupied by their kin or friends, and secondly, to the free lands "back of beyond" where no one else had ventured.

Agents there were, no doubt in plenty, to urge migration in order to sell land; masters of ships were eager to secure passengers from all Irish ports and "sell" them for seven years' service on arriving at Philadelphia in order to recoup their passage money. Yet the most far-reaching force in actually jostling loose these canny folk from the economic servility under which their ancestors had lived was the reports sent back from America by the vanguard.

Dear Sister [wrote one of these, Robert Parke, in 1725]: I desire thee may tell my old friend Samuel Thornton that he could give so much credit to my words & find no iffs nor ands in my Letter that in Plain terms he could not do better than to Come here. . . . We plowed up our Sumer's fallows in May & June, with a Yoak of Oxen & 2 horses & they goe with as much Ease as Double the number in Ireland.[7]

As this race sifted into York, Adams, Bucks, Lancaster, Lebanon, Northampton, Montgomery, Dauphin, and on to Mifflin and Juniata and far-away Washington counties in Pennsylvania, they

[5] Chase, *op. cit.*, p. 26.   [6] *Ibid.*
[7] Quoted in A. C. Meyers, *Immigration of the Irish Quakers*, p. 70.

were influenced by an ancient aversion to "dry" limestone lands. Of course many pitched and remained on such soil, but prejudice dominated so frequently that it became almost axiomatic, and in many cases even where the limestone zones were occupied by Scotch-Irish we find that the first comers later sold out to Germans and went on. Careful local study of this phenomenon would doubtless bring out many interesting facts.

Inherent aversion to being redemptioners was a signal trait in this people.[8] This drive for independence undoubtedly helps to explain that peculiar liking for the frontier which the Scot showed; his paucity of means operated to this same end; the Scotch-Irish man did his full share of squatting, and showed in some historic instances a determination to drive his own bargain and move on if he failed to win his point.[9]

No rule or set of rules will explain why German, Scot, Welsh, Irish, or English reacted as they did to such an environment as Pennsylvania. Only a great burden of evidence, made up by careful local study, can give a basis for any generalization. There are good indications, however, which can be used as guides.[10]

[8] Robert Parke, who is quoted above, gave this advice for his friend to follow: "The best way for him to do is to pay what money he Can Conveniently Spare at that side & engage himself to Pay the rest at this Side & when he Comes here if he Can get no friend to lay down the money for him, when it Comes to the worst, he may hire out 2 or 3 Children." (*Ibid.*)

[9] In Hulbert, *Washington and the West,* is found a specific case of men of this character. These squatted on Washington's lands on Miller's Run, Washington County, Pennsylvania. In 1784 the General visited them in person, dickered with them as to the price he would take, and upon their refusal to pay evicted them by process of law. The legal papers are still extant and the subject is worth more detailed treatment than I gave it. One's opinion is biased by the fact that, although too pious to treat with their distinguished visitor on Sabbath, their scruples did not prevent some of them from setting fire to all improvements before they left, or destroying a building that Washington had had built on the land before they arrived. The case is of added interest because Washington took a careful account of improvements made by his nonpaying guests. This gives us a rare opportunity to see exactly what an isolated pioneer group far out on the frontier could accomplish in a definite space of time by way of improving land and building houses and barns. The price Washington placed on the lands was an annual rental of £10 per hundred acres per annum.

[10] The basis for the following analysis of zones of racial occupation of Pennsylvania will be found in Sherman Day, *Historical Collection of Pennsylvania* (Philadelphia, 1843), under the heads of the counties mentioned.

RALSTON AND BROWN STOCKADE, IN THE "IRISH SETTLEMENT," PENNSYLVANIA

One line of Scotch movement came up from Newcastle County, Maryland, where the tithes made settlement for them uncomfortable.[11] Yet as early as 1729, when John and James Hendricks went into the Kreutz Creek region west of the Susquehanna, the land they took up had been improved by unknown earlier arrivals; but this region eventually became German, while in the Pidgeon Hills the "York Barrens" became predominantly English and Scotch. The distribution of German and Scotch in York County varied generally with soil types. Dotting this region were the Conowingo or Serpentine "barrens," State Line barrens, Nottingham barrens, and the York Barrens just mentioned. Being destitute of trees, these lands were judged far below their real value. Portions of them are yet of slight value, due not to climate, nor to an entire absence of lime, but to the large amount of magnesia present.[12] Yet the Scotch found in this discounted country soil in which wheat sown gave from eighteen to twenty bushels to the acre the first year, and from which, by rotating rye, corn, and oats, in that order, and leaving the land idle for a year or two, good wheat crops could again be secured.

Near the center of this county a strip of limestone, six or seven miles in width, crosses it trending southwest. This soon drew a large German population. Surrounded as it is by soil of another character, it offers a good subject for study by those who have access to the local land records from this point of view of racial occupation.

The southerly origin of the Scotch-Irish movement is indicated in Lancaster County by the names of the townships Donegal and Paxton, and the rivalry in this county between "Irish" and Germans is a familiar story to readers of Pennsylvania's history. From Chester County to the eastward the Welsh and English Quakers crept into Lancaster, as is indicated by the name of Sadsbury township which they occupied. Northampton offers in its rich Pennsylvania Valley a similar display of Scotch-Irish aversion to the "dry" limestone lands:

[11] *Pennsylvania Magazine of History* (1901), p. 497.
[12] F. W. Pennell, "Flora of the Conowingo Barrens" *Proceedings of the Academy of Natural Science of Philadelphia* (1910), pp. 541–543.

The earlier settlers of this county [writes Sherman Day] were emigrants from the north of Ireland; they generally avoided the limestone lands (there known as *the dry lands*, and little esteemed), preferring the slaty hills of Mount Bethel and Allen townships, where they found pure springs of water near the surface.[13]

Describing the founding of Easton, the same writer adds a further word on this subject: "In the early days of the town, all the limestone lands between it and Bethlehem, back from the streams, were termed *the dry lands* and *the barrens;* and as there were no springs to be found upon them they were considered unfit for residence, and were left in a wild unsettled state."[14]

Our previous suggestion that the Scotch-Irish aversion to the best lands on the grounds that they could not afford them, therefore does not always hold true, though it may have played a part in specific cases. Where they had free field, as in Juniata County, they chose the "slate lands bordering the mountains, watered by clear and copious springs" in preference to the "limestone lands, where the waters sunk beneath the surface and expensive wells were consequently required."[15]

Another factor in the aversion of the Scots to certain limestone regions was the fact that they were heavily wooded. The Germans, like the Yankees, were familiar with wooded countries; the Scots, like our southerners when they went west, preferred the prairie to forested tracts. Day says, with reference to the entrance of Scotch-Irish into the northern parts of Lancaster and Chester:

A large number of Scotch-Irish, in consequence of the limestone land being liable to frost, and heavily wooded, seated themselves along the northern line of the counties of Chester and Lancaster, well known at an early period by the name of the "Chestnut Glade." The Germans purchased their little improvements, and were not intimidated either by the difficulty of clearing, the want of water, or the liability to frost, which at this period was experienced every month in the year.[16]

The occupation by the Scotch-Irish of both the Chestnut Country in New Hampshire and of the "Chestnut Glade" in Pennsyl-

[13] *Historical Collection of Pennsylvania*, p. 510.
[14] *Ibid.*, p. 512.
[15] *Ibid.*, p. 383.   [16] *Ibid.*, p. 395.

vania was interesting; but it was more than a coincidence—how much more is a question for students in a position to analyze scrupulously both local documents and the character of specific regions. The present purpose is accomplished by adding, to the total of other reasons, that the Scot was preëminently not only a frontiersman but a far frontiersman, the fact of his plain predilection for the kind of soils which lay beyond the fertile limestone "islands" in Pennsylvania. He may often have been unable to buy good land; yet the "poor fund," even in Scotch colonies far from seaboard, went begging for grantees; he was too rich in that native sagacity which overcomes want, to be "poor." Nature and the mountains were a harsh master but they found in the Scot one who could drive a hard bargain and who never cried for quarter. It was trebly important for America that the force of circumstance should have led this bold people to the confines of the border when it did, and that the environment was one into which they could fit with a lusty good grace.

Thus across Chester and Lancaster and York, strode Scot and Irish; they crossed the Susquehanna and South Mountain; they filed in companies, and by ones and twos went beyond the Appalachian Valley and banked themselves against the Alleghenies. Pennsylvania would not have been Pennsylvania without both the Palatinate German and the Ulsterite, the Irish, Welsh, Huguenot, and English. Each race measurably fulfilled its peculiar destiny and sought its natural environment.

The Scot and Irish made the zone behind Philadelphia peculiar in many particulars, but in nothing so much as its unexampled prosperity. It is necessary to emphasize this from our present point of view of American history, because only a thoroughly prosperous colony could, in those troubled days before the Old French War, have sent out a crucial migration.

Chapter XVI

THE KEYSTONE STATE

WHETHER Pennsylvania is a "keystone state" geographically may be questioned, but that it is a keystone state historically becomes clear when the matter is examined from the point of view of the soil as a factor in American expansion.

A region which produced great crops was inevitably destined to see an important development in methods of transportation. That New England should have developed at Salem and Marblehead and Gloucester a fleet unequaled on our seaboard is explained by her fisheries. Had her meadows produced such wheat as grew in Pennsylvania, something like the Conestoga wagon would have been developed there as it was in those wheat fields. Had Pennsylvania's men been engaged as wholly in commercial matters of the type that interested the Yankee merchants, the equivalent of the Concord coach would have been developed there. Of course wagons and coaches were well known in both of these provincial regions, but the vehicle which represented most typically the one was not typical of the other.

The influence of the tremendous crops of grain which came to be raised in Pennsylvania with the development of transportation in this country deserves its own historian. We have referred to the immediate interest men took in the breeding of horses in Chester County, to the extent of being able to export them even before Penn's arrival in 1682. With the opening of every new acre of limestone soil more provender was raised and the need of beasts of burden in order to market the surplus grew greater. To this grain country came horses and cattle from all directions to be fattened; it became a profitable investment to purchase stock where it was lean and cheap and fatten it where grain was abundant and inexpensive. As early as 1758 Governor Dinwiddie of Virginia proposed to his legislature to pass "a short Law" which would prevent Pennsylvania drovers from coming into the Valley and buying the cattle which Colonel Washington sorely needed for his bastioned garrisons.[1] When Braddock was marching toward the French in 1755 he depended on "the back parts of Maryland and Virginia" for wagons. When all that could be obtained were gathered, the number proved to be twenty-five—and not a few of these were wholly unfit for a journey!

Franklin happened to be at Braddock's headquarters at Frederick at this time and informed Braddock that "in Pennsylvania . . . almost every farmer had his wagon." This resulted in Franklin's well-known activity in putting Braddock's army on wheels. The "Advertisement" which he issued "To the Inhabitants of the Counties of Lancaster, York and Cumberland" resulted in his securing 150 wagons and 259 pack horses in two weeks' time.[2]

In the Revolution Washington looked to this granary of America for the salvation of the patriot cause. From it Congress chose the gingerbread maker Christopher Ludwig to be Baker General to the army, with the title of "Superintendent of Bakers and Director of Baking."[3] To Joseph Reed, Washington wrote on May 28, 1780: "Either Pennsylvania must give us all the aid we ask of her, or we can undertake nothing . . . the fate of these States hangs upon it."

These illustrations suggest how truly Pennsylvania was the granary of the colonies in both 1755 and 1780. A logical development was for her to surpass her rivals in improving methods of getting her crops to market. Thus an insistent demand for improved methods of transportation in this region arose earlier than in other parts of the seaboard. In the decade from 1750 to 1760, even when the frontiers were in the tumult of Indian warfare, a canal between the Schuylkill and the Susquehanna was being discussed, and in 1762 a route was surveyed and leveled for it by way of Tulpehocken and Swatara creeks. Pontiac's Rebellion and then the Revolution intervened; it was not until 1792 that work was actually begun, and the canal was not completed until 1827. That here should have been surveyed our first canal of considerable

---

[1] S. M. Hamilton, *Letters to Washington*, I, 373.
[2] John Bigelow (ed.), *Autobiography of Benjamin Franklin*, pp. 303–307.
[3] *Pennsylvania Magazine of History*, XVI, 343.

length, and that about fifteen miles of it should have been completed before 1795, is an interesting commentary on the enterprise of the men of this region; no such line of transportation existed elsewhere in our land.

It was also in this region that John Fitch of Connecticut made some of his earliest experiments in steamboat navigation. In August, 1785, he launched on a rivulet in Bucks County, his model propelled by an engine which moved an endless chain to which paddle wheels were attached; and in Lancaster was born the man who, working on Fitch's models, finally assembled our first practical steamboat—Robert Fulton. It was a neighbor of Fulton's and Fitch's, Oliver Evans, who built and drove the first steam engine on an American (Pennsylvanian) highway and who anticipated the belief of Stephenson that steam-driven vehicles would travel best on railed tracks.

The time was not ripe for the development of these methods of transportation, however; if it had been, no doubt the crops of the Palatinate German settlements of Pennsylvania would have been first in this country to have found new conveyances to market. The recourse was to improved highways, and it is not surprising that the first macadamized road built in the United States should have been the Lancaster Turnpike joining Lancaster County and the Pennsylvania metropolis.

The Lancaster Turnpike Road Company was chartered in 1792 and the road was built at a cost of $465,000; its length was sixty-two miles, and its cost was about the same as the sum expended on the fifteen miles of the Union Canal then being constructed. In no case had such sums been spent by any other state on similar works of internal improvement.

The strategic position of the Lancaster road and the abundance of limestone at hand for its construction made it an instant success. Men foresaw this. The subscription books were opened at eleven o'clock in the morning, and by midnight 2,226 shares had been subscribed, each investor paying down thirty dollars in cash. Like the Erie Canal, which possessed an equally strategic location, the Lancaster road was such a success that it led to the formation of scores of incorporated roads which were not favored by having a fertile region at one end and a great city at the other, and which consequently had no such history as did that famous turnpike.

We have given in some detail these facts concerning the development of eastern Pennsylvania in the last years of this century because they reflect vividly the wealth, energy, and stability of the most powerful agricultural region in America at this period. Nothing illustrates the prosperity and growth of a region more clearly than its development of transportation; in this respect the early history of Pennsylvania stands unequaled.

At the same time other factors, aside from that of crops to be moved, played their part in such development. The steep, rocky hills of New England were not common here; the land was, rather, of the "rolling" type. Moreover, as has been mentioned before, the limestone lands offered ideal road-building materials on the spot. Again, the early mining and working of iron was a strong influence in producing any kind of transportation in which iron was always a requisite. When proper account of these factors is taken, then and then only is one able to give to the Pennsylvania soils and their products full credit for an era of development unknown elsewhere at that time in all our colonies.

We have no data of definite character to show how this prosperity developed from, let us say, that day in 1709 when Lancaster County received its first immigrant. When we see such notable prosperity, however, as was apparent in that part of the country a century later, and realize how much it was derived from the soil, we glimpse a field of study of the greatest interest and value. There is not a township in the region mentioned which does not afford material for a fresh survey of local history based on the relation of man to environment.

Here we find the first link in a chain of expansive movements which made possible an American Republic of continental dimensions. This polyglot region was one of the main breeding grounds of America's most crucial expansive movement. When one studies with care the relationship of this Pennsylvania to the planting of a population in the far-famed valley of Virginia, in Tennessee, and in Kentucky; when one traces critically the great seams of lime-

stone soils which stream southward from York and Chambersburg across the Potomac to the greater limestone oases where
Nashville, Tennessee, and Lexington, Kentucky, arose; when one
assays without bias the quality of leadership in the Southwest
which had its origin in Pennsylvania (as in the case of the Boones,
Finleys, Lewis', and Bryans, the Lincolns, Harts, and Hankses)
one will be led to feel that no similarly limited region exerted the
same timely influence on national destiny as it did.

Woven deeply in the record of this Scotch-Irish and Palatinate
German Pennsylvania, are the strands which make up this drama
of early expansion. As primary factors one must rank the rich
soils which have their origin here. We have seen that as the Pennsylvania soil series encounter the mountain barrier they swing
sharply to the southward; crossing the narrow neck of Maryland
and spanning the Potomac, they throw long tongues up a score of
that river's southern tributaries; the one reaching up the Shenandoah through the valley of Virginia, passes on to end only in the
rich central valleys of Tennessee and Kentucky. That this blue
grass pathway might well become a pathway of empire is evident.

If this was to be true, there had to be driving forces behind
as well as magnetic influences to lure it forward. Both existed,
in large measure. They have not perhaps been studied with the
scrupulous care which their consequences justify; they cannot be
estimated properly until all the factors of environment, physical,
political, and social, are taken into consideration.

Probably the most salient of these factors was the crowding
of a heterogeneous population that began in 1725 upon the rich
Pennsylvania region. By that time reports of the character of the
Pennsylvania soils had been well circulated abroad. Two years
later the colony passed a law that ships' masters must take the
names of immigrants and that the latter must swear allegiance to
the colony's king.[4] As we have suggested, the figures of this influx
have been exaggerated, but the result has not. What the figures do
not show is the amount of capital which many of these immigrants
brought with them; the rapidity with which such counties as Mont-

---

[4] I. D. Rupp, *A Collection of Thirty Thousand Names,* gives the roll of early
German immigration to Pennsylvania as well as to other colonies down to 1775.

gomery and Lancaster were occupied has a significance not properly recognized; within twenty years after Montgomery acquired
its principal quota of colonists, its lands were practically all taken
up. How far the movement spread is shown by Rupp, who gives the
names of more than seventy Germans alone who were massacred
north of Blue Mountain in the Old French War which began in
1755. As to the Scotch-Irish, who pressed on still farther into the
wilderness, no figures are obtainable, but it is believed that their
numbers were greater and their loss larger. Oddly enough, of the
68,872 Germans whose names are tabulated by Rupp as arriving
between the years 1727 and 1775, about one-half came in the six
years preceding the outbreak of that war, 1749–54. The first considerable number to arrive in one year was in 1732 when 2,168
came in; in 1738 the number of arrivals was 3,115; then eleven
years afterward came the rush mentioned above, bringing nearly
32,000 in six years. This, it is to be remembered, is only the overseas immigration of Palatinate Germans and Swiss; the immigration of these races from other parts of the colonies where their agricultural experiments had failed, or that of other nationalities from
any source, is not given, nor is the natural increase.

With a rapidly increasing multitude of newcomers, many of
them in a position to purchase or to begin the purchase of land,
it is evident that there was to be scant room for the squatter in
the fertile zone of Pennsylvania. The price of land, of course,
varied with its supposed productivity, taken in connection with
its location with reference to market. The low price charged by
William Penn became memorable within a decade. The Robert
Parke whose whimsical advice to his neighbor in Ireland we have
quoted paid £350 for five hundred acres in old Chester County
before 1725; this agrees fairly closely with the value the Penns
placed upon their Conestoga Manor lands, namely £40 per hundred acres. This was the price of the best lands; for ordinary land
the common price was £10 per hundred acres in 1719 with two
shillings quitrent; by 1732 it had jumped to £15 6s per hundred
acres with a quitrent of half a penny an acre. This rise in price
had two effects: it tended to drive the poor immigrant or the redemptioner who was without funds beyond the fertile zone into

the far frontier, and it induced many of the first settlers to take advantage of the high price to make an honest penny. They sold out and moved into the interior, where for one-tenth of their suddenly acquired capital they could secure as much land—and land potentially as valuable. Such we may suppose might have been the case with the Boones, who very early gave up their holdings in Pennsylvania and fared down the long blue grass pathway to a clearing on the Yadkin in North Carolina, or with the young John Lincoln, first of the "shirt-sleeve era of Lincolns" who struck out from the old home in Chester County and made his new planting in Rockingham County, Virginia, in the midst of the Old French War.

There were also social and political reasons which both made it easy for many to leave this region and rendered newcomers quite satisfied to seek further. With the death of William Penn the amicable relations that had been maintained with the Pennsylvania Indians did not continue; this was inevitable under any circumstances with an increased population. The situation was made worse, in York County, for instance, because it led to interstate troubles. As early as 1720 Maryland speculators were extending their claims north of what was finally established as the Maryland-Pennsylvania line. The objections of the Conestoga Indians resulted in Maryland's granting Pennsylvania the right to survey the Springettsbury Manor opposite Columbia, better known as Keith's Survey, which extended the Pennsylvania boundary line beyond the Susquehanna. This exposed the fact that Marylanders had pitched on land as high up in Pennsylvania as the latitude of Philadelphia. In fact it has been said, with no little truth, that "the early settlement of York County commenced in quarrels, and the effects of those quarrels have descended to our day."[5]

That the Scotch-Irish and Germans were no more harmonious than the Yankee and the Scot is in evidence on many a page of Pennsylvania's history, one notorious instance being the raid of the "Paxton boys" on Lancaster in the interest of Indians imprisoned there.

---

[5] Rupp, *Historical Collection,* p. 693. For further references to these troubles see *ibid.*, pp. 262–263, 692, 700.

And so between the rising prices of lands, the inrush of settlers, the difficulties encountered by those who did not know where Maryland's jurisdiction ended and where Pennsylvania's began, the awakening of serious Indian hostility, and the rivalry that arose between Scot and German, it is seen that motive enough existed for migration even from Pennsylvania's limestone Garden of Eden. At a very early date other reasons existed to cause dissatisfaction. The business methods of William Penn were disastrously loose. The "old rights" of first purchasers who never appeared either in person or by proxy, were granted over again by deeds of lease and release; many grants were never surveyed and some were never even located; many persons who had purchased as a speculation never visited their lands or secured deeds for them; the papers on which the land records were made were filed along with papers relating to every other colonial matter and became a part of a maze of uncalendared, undocumented, and unindexed papers; to find a desired paper might mean weeks of searching.

The lax way in which this important business was conducted worked definite hardships. It resulted in the Penns being endlessly defrauded by speculators and sharpers; and it led to hundreds of others being made doubtful of the validity of their deeds. This of itself was, to many, sufficient inducement to sell out and let others fight the battle of title; and it was another reason why many did not choose to buy land here at all. When Thomas Penn arrived in the colony in 1732 and began the difficult, if not impossible, task of righting wrongs long since committed—of evicting honest men who had unwittingly purchased dishonest claims, and dishonest men who had acquired fair title by improper means —he produced results more notable for turmoil than for actual justice meted out.

At exactly this time came the stories of the equal fertility of the southland to which the limestone paths seemed to lead. The Indians in that remote part of the world had always been reported as friendly to the Pennsylvania traders who visited them; fabulous stories were afloat that Maryland companies were prepared to sell good lands at £5 per hundred acres; that Virginia was offering free grants of a thousand acres in the valley to each family who would migrate, and of Lord Granville's offer of a quarter section (640 acres) in North Carolina for three shillings. Following these rumors came men who had received grants from the governor of Virginia and who had visited the land; their stories were based on first-hand knowledge of the character and quality of soils.

To the growing thousands of new immigrants just landed in Pennsylvania, to the discontented who had been ousted from lands which they supposed they had fairly acquired, to the squatters who were now told (as those were, for instance, in the "York Barrens") that they must decamp, to all who had suffered or feared they would suffer from the rivalry between Maryland and Pennsylvania, and to all who were offered "fortunes" for lands which they had secured cheaply or free of charge, these rumors made a tremendously strong appeal.

Lancaster and York now became the outfitting stations for one of the most interesting migrations in our history. As this migration now becomes the subject of our study, and as we review the humble but vitally important pageant which took its rise here to halt only on the shores of the Pacific, let us keep well in mind both the factors which were expulsive within the rich Pennsylvania country, and those which were magnetic—soils beyond the Potomac and even beyond Cumberland Gap, drawing to them eager men. It is hardly too much to say that no such movement could have started from any other part of the American colonies. We have seen something of the story of the development of this region and appreciate how it could have become the base of such a migratory wave. It had thousands of prosperous farms on which fathers could afford to equip sons and sons-in-law for the adventure of migration; it had flocks and herds, horses and oxen to spare for those who wished to go; and it had tools of iron to hew the way.

Moreover, migration was following, in every sense, lines of least resistance. The first reports of explorers and speculators beyond the Potomac attested the fact that the soils, both limestone and slate, on which Scot and German had thrived in Pennsylvania, were continuous in that direction; that the country to which they led was as ideal for general agriculture and for fruit

and grain as the homeland by the Conestoga or Kittanning; and
that for raising stock it even surpassed anything known in the
North. The succulent blue grass of that southland drove out
other growths and mounted to the very summits of the mountains
which were called "balds" for that reason. And in such a climate
cattle could winter in the open without great risk; when it snowed
they could paw the snow away and find "blue grass beneath it still
green."

We see then an interesting correlation between a rich and popu-
lous region to the north, where motives for migration were plenti-
ful, and an equally rich valley to the south which attracted with
the magnetism that only well-known soils and well-known vegetation could exert upon a distinctly agricultural people.

In no more important sense was Pennsylvania a Keystone state
than in the position of its limestone valleys with reference to the
valley of Virginia, and in the manhood and resources which she
could early add to the first tide of American migration.

Chapter XVII

THE GRAND ADVANCE

FROM our previous glimpses into the valley of Virginia it is plain, despite the lack of information which handicaps the inquirer, that interest in western Virginia was rapidly increasing in those stirring years from 1725 to 1730.

We know little as yet of the men who played the spectacular rôle of heralds to announce to the world the luxuriant fertility of the valley. They doubtless were Indian traders like John Van Metre who traded among the Delawares and followed them on their excursions against their southern enemies. This knowing Hollander, who hailed from near Kingston, New York, was more impressed with the character of the soil and vegetation south of the Potomac than with any he had seen elsewhere in his travels.

The region was probably being honeycombed by explorers at this time. Van Metre, however, was the kind of man evidently to see the vision in the large and to go about its realization in a businesslike way. His route to the Potomac had probably been through the rich Pennsylvania region, for presumably it was only by coming this way that he could have met the two Pennsylvanians, one an Alsatian and the other a Huguenot, who came to play such an important part in the history of the valley of Virginia.

One of these was the prosperous Baron Hans Joist Heydt, formerly of Strasbourg in Alsace, who had come to America some twenty years before in his own ships with a colony of people, and who now lived beside the Schuylkill. That he was a good American in the making is proved by the fact that he was now no longer Baron Heydt but plain Joist Hite—a name which has a prominent place in the histories of Virginia, Tennessee, and Kentucky. Another Pennsylvanian who was interested in Van Metre's account of the land was John Lewis, who eventually became the famous "Lord of the Hills" about Staunton. Lewis possibly was interested in that southern zone before meeting either Hite or Van Metre, for the William Lynn who belonged to the company which in 1727 got the Bath County grant, was his brother-in-law.[1]

Hite and Lewis were excellent men to inspire a "Grand Advance," characters of sterling worth who could create the confidence necessary to rally adventurous men for any undertaking. Whether Hite purchased some or all of Van Metre's grant, whether he received one of the "minor rights" which, it is said, William Penn's heirs and John Fenwick held, or whether he and his friends set about securing rights solely on their own initiative, are points to be cleared up.

At any rate Governor Gooch's castle in Williamsburg was stormed simultaneously by this whole group of Pennsylvanians, as well as by the Van Metres of New Jersey. In 1730 the Governor of Virginia issued grants of thirty thousand acres to John Van Metre, ten thousand of which were to be located at "the places called by the name of Cedar Lick and Stony Lick" in old Frederick County in the valley. This shows that Van Metre must have been on the spot and knew precisely the very land he wanted. His twenty-thousand-acre grant was to be located between the lands of Robert Carter and Mann Page (Virginians who had already received 50,000 and 8,007 acres respectively) provided he should settle twenty families on the land within two years.[2]

Isaac Van Metre, son of John, petitioned for and received a grant of ten thousand acres on condition that he should settle ten German families on the land; this land lay between Cedar Creek and the future site of Winchester.

The "peticon of Rob't McKay and & Joost Heyd" was one of the largest presented to the Governor; it was for one hundred thousand acres, the land to be chosen between the grants made to Van Metre, Stover, Fishback, and others.[3] They were to bring one family on the land for each one thousand acres.[4]

Alexander Ross and Morgan Bryan received a grant as large as

---

[1] *Virginia Magazine of History,* XIII (October, 1905), 114.

[2] *Ibid.,* pp. 115–117.

[3] *Ibid.,* p. 134.

[4] *Ibid.,* p. 354; it is estimated by Mr. Kemper that Hite and McKay eventually brought 250 persons to this grant.

the McKay-Hite grant and on the same terms; Jacob Stover received one for ten thousand acres. Stover is the man who is alleged to have "adopted" and named all his cows, pigs, and chickens before migrating in order to keep the land in the family! It is believed that all these were from Pennsylvania or New Jersey. It is not at all unlikely that Robert McKay was Hite's brother-in-law, as the latter's wife was of Scotch-Irish ancestry; the wife of John Lewis was Margaret Lynn of that stock.

Legislative grants were one thing, actual migration was another. This is what adds interest and picturesqueness to the little party of sixteen families which now moved out from the York Barrens among the Pidgeon Hills near the Susquehanna, early in 1732, led by Hite, McKay, and Lewis.[5] In the party were Hite's sons-in-law, Paul Froman, George Bowman, and Jacob Chrisman; also Robert Green, William Duff, and Peter Stephens, founder of Stephensburg; the names of Allen, Hoge, Lewis, Wilson, White, Van Metre, Van Swearingen, all to become well-known names from the Blue Ridge to the Mississippi, are given as probable members. Their route was the old trail, no doubt well marked if overgrown, leading from the York Barrens to the ancient ford across the Potomac at Shepherdstown.

No rule is observable in the way these families occupied this Land of Goshen; some bought rights of Hite who settled on the Opequon; Stephens founded historic Stephensburg; Chrisman located Chrisman's Spring two miles to the southward; Bowman went on to Cedar Creek six miles south of Chrisman; Froman took up land on the same stream eight miles northwest of Bowman; McKay pitched on Crooked Run eight miles northwest of Stephensburg.

Those who for various reasons have sought to show that the

[5] In view of a world-wide interest that will be awakened in the Bicentenary in 1932 of the birth of Washington, it is in point to observe that this initial movement, which may loosely be termed the beginning of westward American migration, occurred in the very year that he was born. Accidentally, of course, but interestingly enough, the first determined movement from the Mississippi Valley toward the Pacific Coast overland, on the part of men thinking in other terms than solely those of the fur trader, took place exactly one hundred years later, in 1832, when the Joist Hites of that day—Nathaniel Wyeth, John Ball, and Captain Bonneville—formed parties to cross the plains and Rockies.

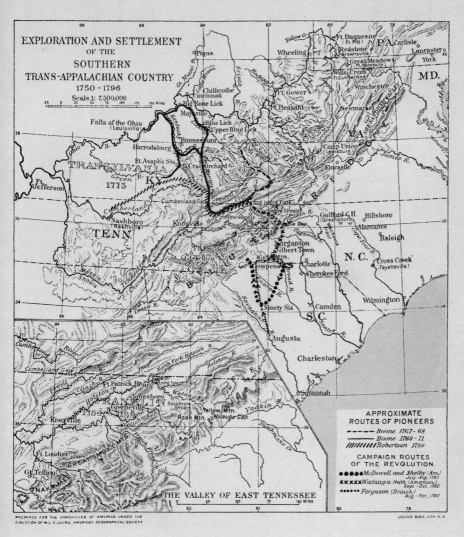

THE SOUTHWEST OF BOONE, ROBERTSON, AND SEVIER

By permission, from *The Chronicles of America,* published by Yale University Press

Hite colony is not, in the light of present data, entitled to the honor of settling the famed valley of Virginia, do not glimpse the thing in its entirety. Individuals were unquestionably living already on the rich lands in that region. Numerous grants had been made numbering perhaps a full million acres before the Hite-McKay-Lewis party bade farewell to Pidgeon Hills and the Barrens; but this was largely the work of absentee speculators. That Pennsylvania party formed the vanguard of American migration to Virginia, to Tennessee, to Kentucky, and to the Pacific. In old New England phraseology there were "goers" and "stayers" in most colonization enterprises. These men of the Hite party were "goers" —they were home builders. In them we see the first organized advance of American civilization into the West.

The method of occupation was, it is evident, more of the New England type than of the "plantation" type, as these "Windsors" and "Wethersfields" and "Hartfords" of the Northern Neck of Virginia now sprang into existence; and as in the case of their northern prototypes, good lands dictated absolutely where settlements should be made. Some of these pioneers purchased land, some became tenants of purchasers, and many squatted on lands which pleased them. Others bought from Ross and some from Stover; some bought from the Fairfaxes; and many took land independently by old Virginia "corn rights" or "cabin rights" or "tomahawk claim" systems. These different ways of attaining the same thing—landownership—mark the difference between the New England episode and the Virginian. The movement soon became a "rush," acquiring momentum from pioneers who undoubtedly also forged up the Rappahannock from the Virginia Piedmont. It was the "Grand Advance" of all nationalities—English, German, Scotch-Irish, Irish, and Huguenot. While dogged pioneers were piercing the Allegheny barrier in every direction, and while fur traders with their strings of pack horses were deepening every trail from eastern Pennsylvania to the Ohio, such concerted action, such crowding forward of masses of people, was nowhere else witnessed on any such scale as that which fell beneath the eyes of Hite and Lewis along this blue grass pathway to the southwest.

Little did it seem to these vanguards that it was a "westward" movement. Little did they conceive that among this stream of humanity which they had piloted to the Shenandoah, were the Boones and Lincolns from Pennsylvania who should plant good seed in that far-away meadow land of Kentucky. Little did they fancy that the tousle-headed boy, Felix Grundy, born in that cabin on Back Creek in old Berkeley was to come from Tennessee to be attorney-general of the United States in 1838; or that John Miller on Tuscarora Creek was to become governor of Missouri; or that the sprightly young Tom Worthington, born in an "old fields" cabin, was to become governor of Ohio; or that Abraham, Adam, Hezekiah, and John McKnitt Alexander, and Avery, Balch, Brevard, Barry, and Davidson—all sojourners at some time, probably within hailing distance of Hite and Lewis on this famous southward track—should be signers of a Macklenburg "Declaration" to be issued in the North Carolina highlands. The pathway was the "long way 'round" but it led to the West; and when twenty-three years later the Great Virginian who was born in this year of Hite's migration (1732) to old Frederick, was saving the remnant of Braddock's army beside the Monongahela, there were stations on this pathway located almost a whole degree of longitude farther west than "Braddock's Field."

In considering this movement we have reversed the order followed elsewhere and described it without particular reference to soils and climate as primary factors. No such general movement could have been inspired by any single cause. The mountain ranges in central Pennsylvania blocked the straight pathway of expansion westward. The French and the Indians served as human barriers perhaps equally important; the two together formed, at the same time, an insuperable obstacle. Granting this, we must also note the attraction of these limestone avenues across the Potomac as a line of magnetic influence and the inviting character of the valley of Virginia that powerfully affected the spontaneity of the immigrant movement as well as its direction. It changed what might have been a more or less aimless dispersal into a "Grand Advance" because it led to a definite goal.

The valley of Virginia is from fifteen to thirty miles in width and three hundred and ten miles in length, an area of about five thousand square miles. Perhaps the most important factor in its topography, from our point of view, is that it is not a single valley in the sense that the James and Connecticut are single valleys. The boundary line on the east of it is the Blue Ridge; on the west the boundary is sometimes the second, and sometimes the third range of parallel mountains, thus making it more than a "valley." Had it been only that, the pathway of migration would perhaps have been effectually blocked by engrossed estates which might have developed according to the practice followed in the valleys of the James and the York.

One is scarcely impressed with this vital fact until he maps the innumerable Potomac tributaries which enter that river from the south between Patterson's Creek and the Blue Ridge barrier at Harper's Ferry. Over such a region great grants of land could be made by pen and seal and gay ribbons, such as the Fairfax Grant, but the topography made it a typical "poor man's country," to be developed, if at all, through personal initiative and plucky pioneering—the ideal land (merely from the standpoint of topography) for the individual prospector and immigrant, but not an environment favorable to the absentee landlord. Large and splendid plantations came into existence, it is true, in the immediate valley of the Shenandoah; but for the most part the country into which the migration from Pennsylvania and Piedmont Virginia poured was essentially a land of small farms, and had been so designed centuries before.

The limestone valley of Pennsylvania breaks across the Potomac here; forming long fingers, it reaches up the southern Potomac tributaries in varying lengths, or continues, as we have seen, in wide or narrow streaks far to the southward, especially up the Shenandoah and on toward the James, New, and heads of the Tennessee. The first reports of this region were of the section between North Mountain and the Shenandoah, and described it as one vast prairie; Kercheval, annalist of the valley, reports old residents to have affirmed that much of Berkeley, Jefferson, and Frederick counties was denuded of timber by the aborigines; and one of these related that the grass was so luxuriant that in places the rider could reach and tie it while on horseback.[6]

Of the rich Hagerstown series of soils Virginia has, by present surveys, one hundred thousand acres of the stony loam, an equal amount of loam, and over half as much sandy loam. "The most productive valley phase," Mr. Whitney states, "occurs in the large valley between the Blue Ridge and the Allegheny Mountains."[7] It was an ideal general farming country and well named by Washington "The Garden of America." Blue grass was indigenous here and it became "the home of the stock-raiser and dairyman"; the heavier clay lands, rich in fertilizing ingredients, always well repaid "the labor spent on them in crops of corn or other grain"; the light slaty lands were noted for their wheat crops, while the poorer ridges afforded excellent grazing for sheep and cattle.[8]

Thus a sufficient variety of soil to please any man was present here. The Pennsylvania background was a source from which to draw all the initial flocks and herds. The main valley itself rose 1,621 feet from mouth to source of the Shenandoah, thus neutralizing, in the matter of temperature, its southerly trend. It had a mean temperature of 54° and a growing season of from five and a half to six months. No more ideal avenue and outlet for a Pennsylvania and Virginia Piedmont could be imagined. The valley is sometimes blessed with what many believed to be a handicap—a blanket of snow which usually mantles it in midwinter. The covering which this afforded the grasses and grains protected them against midwinter cold and modified the effect of sudden thaws on occasional warm days.[9]

Too much can hardly be made of these factors because of their influence on stock raising; it was always comparatively easy to promote migration in a direction which cattle could take, and to a country where they would thrive. Thus reinforced pioneers always had a food supply on which they could depend. To what degree this industry prospered, one of Braddock's officers who

---

[6] S. Kercheval, *Valley of Virginia*.   [7] Whitney, *op. cit.*, p. 141.
[8] *Virginia: A Synopsis* (Virginia State Board of Agriculture, 1889), p. 13.
[9] G. T. Surface, "Climate and Boundaries of Virginia," *Bulletin of the American Geographical Society*, XXXIX, 96.

left a typically jaundiced but interesting description of the herders of this Potomac region attests; little did the writer realize that the first American cowboys were here laying the basis, with the best means at hand, for the wealth of states in the coming Republic:

From the Heart of the Settlements we are now got into the Cow-Pens, the Keepers of these are very extraordinarily kind of Fellows, they drive up their herds on Horseback, and they had need do so, for their Cattle are near as wild as Deer; a Cow-Pen generally consists of a very large Cottage or House in the Woods, with about four-score or one hundred acres, inclosed with high Rails and divided; a small Inclosure they keep for Corn, for the Family, the rest is the Pasture in which they keep their Calves; but the Manner is far different from any Thing you ever saw; they may perhaps have a Stock of four or five hundred to a thousand head of Cattle belonging to a Cow-Pen, these run as they please in the great Woods, where there are no Inclosures to stop them. In the Month of March the Cows begin to drop their Calves, then the Cow-Pen Master, with all his Men, rides out to see and drive up the Cows with all their new fallen Calves; they being weak cannot run away so as to escape, therefore are easily drove up, and the Bulls and other Cattle follow them; then they put these Calves into the Pasture, and every Morning and Evening suffer the Cows to come and suckle them, which done they let the Cows out into the great Woods to shift for their Food as well as they can; whilst the Calf is suckling one Tit of the Cow, the Woman of the Cow-Pen is milking one of the other Tits, so that she steals some Milk from the Cow, who thinks she is giving it to the Calf; as soon as the Cow begins to go dry, and the Calf grows Strong, they mark them, if they are Males they cut them, and let them go into the Wood. Every Year in September and October they drive up the Market Steers, that are fat and of a proper age, and kill them; they say they are fat in October, but I am sure they are not so in May, June and July; they reckon that out of 100 head of Cattle they can kill about 10 or 12 Steers, and four or five Cows a Year; so they reckon that a Cow-Pen for every 100 head of Cattle brings about 40£ Sterling per Year. The Keepers live chiefly upon Milk, for out of their vast Herds, they do condescend to tame Cows enough to keep their Family in Milk, Whey, Curds, Cheese and Butter; they also have Flesh in Abundance such as it is, for they eat the old Cows and lean Calves that are like to die. The Cow-Pen Men are hardy people, are almost continually on horseback, being obliged to know the Haunts of their Cattle.

You see, Sir, what a wild set of Creatures our English Men grow into, when they lose Society, and it is surprising to think how many Advantages they throw away, which our industrious Country-Men would be glad of. Out of many hundred Cows they will not give themselves the trouble of milking more than will maintain their Family.

It was this "wild set of Creatures" who, on another day, would fight the Britisher and the Tory from King's Mountain to Saratoga. Such glimpses of their life on this borderland are precious. Nature is harsh; what was won from her by the leaders of this advance guard into the Southern Alleghenies was won in honest battle.

Particular notice of the cattle-raising industry, however, is of further value to us. The blue grass empire (which lies above an altitude of 500 feet) was to become important because of flocks and herds. The relationship of this industry to migration has been neglected, but it was a vital asset to these shut-in pioneers not only to depend on herds for milk and meat when necessary, but to be able to raise a "crop" which could go to market on its own legs —over almost any kind of a trail or road. The study of the pea vine and the zone of its growth hereabouts, as well as in the Piedmont of Virginia, would aid in understanding the enormous development of the droves of cattle and pigs in this climate which demanded nothing like the housing in winter which was necessary farther north. An early traveler in the valley mentions the settlements in the rich river bottoms. "They are chiefly settled by Germans," he writes, "who gain a sufficient livelihood by raising stock for the troops [in the Old French War] and sending butter down into the lower parts of the country."[10] It is said that Lord Fairfax once looked with amazement upon an unusually fine drove of hogs which was passing through Winchester from the mountain range to the westward, and affirmed that the region from which they hailed should take the name of Hampshire from the county in England famous for its porkers; and Hampshire it was named, though it may be questioned whether because of the suggestion of the Lord of Greenway Court—for Lord Fairfax was not over-

[10] Quoted in H. Howe, *Collections of Virginia,* p. 468.

popular in these parts in the closing days of the first half of this century.

As early as 1730 Virginia was requesting the King, as we have noted, to draw the line between the Fairfax grant and the colony; Fairfax himself repeated the request in 1733 probably because of the Hite and Lewis migration as well as because of the numerous warrants issued by Virginia to Van Metre, Carter, Hite, and others. In the autumn of 1736 the Fairfax boundary line was marked off from the first spring in the South Branch of the Rappahannock to the head spring in the South Branch of the Potomac. What report these surveyors (three of whom represented each interest involved) made as to soil, climate, character of the country, and its occupants is a subject for investigation.

The entire Hite colony was now settled. The Stover grant on Masinnuton Creek, Page County, was doubtless occupied in part. In 1734 the Allens, Moores, and Whites had settled within twelve miles of Woodstock, and Coburn, Howard, Walker, and Rutledge had made claims to land in the valley of the South Branch; John Van Metre had found the fine lands above "The Trough"; in 1735 the Capon, Lost River, Cedar Creek, and the Opequon had other settlers than those who came with Hite; and as early as 1738 Quaker meetings were being held concerning the Ross warrant on the Opequon between Winchester and Apple Pie Ridge. An Irish colony including the Caseys, Pancakes, and Formans had settled along the South Branch. Isaac Hite, son of John, pitched upon the famous "Long Meadows" on the north branch of the Shenandoah in 1740, and in the same year the Lindsays came in to "Long Marsh" in Frederick County.

Thus it is plain that when the Fairfax agents established their branch land office at Winchester in 1742 they must have faced a perplexing state of affairs. Already Baptists from Van Metre's state—New Jersey—had settled in Berkeley County (near Gerardstown) and a church had been formed there by the Rev. John Gerard. The La Rues and Beelers, also from New Jersey, were located in Frederick County along with the Hamptons from the Maryland East Shore. With Germans on the limestone lands in Page County and extending on from Stephensburg into Rockingham, Scotch-Irish on Back Creek and North Mountain and the Opequon, Baptists in Berkeley, Quakers in Frederick, and Irish everywhere, what English lord could gaze with serenity on his beribboned patent to this land?

Some had bought from Virginia before that colony discovered that the Fairfaxes repudiated the Blue Ridge boundary which, it was supposed, their original grant named as its western bound. Some had bought from the Fairfaxes; scores had bought from some one of the many who secured grants from Governor Gooch; and hundreds had simply squatted.

It is not our province here to enter into a discussion of the questions which must have been argued in all these clearings and "cow-pens" in many languages. The terms offered these settled pioneers by Fairfax (leases for ninety-nine years at twenty shillings annual rental) were considered oppressive.[11]

It is, however, important to our own topic to show how thoroughly occupied the lower Shenandoah had become, and secondly, how naturally there arose here, as in Pennsylvania, unrest, dissatisfaction, and desire to migrate. Expelling forces were, therefore, at work likewise here in the lower valley which tended to drive migration forward. There also existed the siren call of rich lands and free lands on up the Shenandoah along the limestone, blue grass pathway to the Mississippi.

[11] The long struggle between the Hite and Fairfax heirs as to the legality of rights sold to settlers by Joist Hite was settled in 1786 in favor of the Hite grantees. (*Revised Code of Virginia* [1819], II, 346–347.) The price above quoted is exactly the same as asked by Washington for his western lands half a century later (cf. p. ??). His terms, too, were considered oppressive.

Chapter XVIII

BEYOND THE SHENANDOAH

ONE there was, at least, in Joist Hite's company who foresaw more than the prospect presented by this rich country between the mouth of the Shenandoah and Rockingham County. This was the sturdy Huguenot, John Lewis, who with his wife, Margaret Lynn Lewis, had doubtless heard that beyond the Shenandoah lay as fair land as any along its banks.

We have noted that Mrs. Lewis' brother, five years before, had joined with others in securing a patent to lands on the very finger tips of the James; and these far sources of that river formed important links in the Shenandoah-Tennessee line of limestone soils. Undoubtedly the hunters or prospectors who had picked out that fruitful region knew well that the Shenandoah offered by far the easiest pathway; for untold generations this valley road had been traversed by countless red men and probably a great many white men; onward up the river it beckoned, through "Page Land," through the Carter grant of fifty thousand acres, and through the land more recently granted to William Beverly.

Beyond the Shenandoah was the real frontier. It is not possible to believe that Lewis would have ventured toward it had he not known that land there was obtainable from the Indians; how, or when, he learned this is unaccounted for.

In any event, the Lewis party pressed on beyond the zone of the disputed domains of Fairfax or Carter or Beverly, and above the last thread of the Shenandoah, at "Tinkling Spring" near Bellemont, one mile east of Staunton, Lewis and his party established their camp and began their settlement. Who accompanied him is unknown; but if he had with him only his three energetic sons, it would have been ample—for one of those lads, Andrew, was Washington's choice as commander of the Continental Army in 1775.

To those who love the Staunton region the study of this Scotch-Irish movement from Pennsylvania is of superlative interest.

There is no phase of the elements of environment which influenced American migration (which we have treated) which cannot be studied to advantage here—the river trails, the watershed passageways, the soils, and their multiform variations of vegetation from splendid grasses to mighty trees.

Here on the heights above the Shenandoah one finds the ideal vantage point from which to survey one of the most interesting single streams of migration in American history—the Pennsylvania-Kentucky-Tennessee-Mississippi migration. Below in "the Valley" the racial tincture was, originally, distinctively Palatinate German and Swiss. As we leave Rockingham County it becomes as distinctly Scotch-Irish. While it is of little value to draw hard and fast lines, this change in the early domination of a pioneer region forms an interesting and valuable topic of consideration. One very suggestive and enlightening source of information is the study of our church archives; this is particularly true of this line of movement from Pennsylvania to Kentucky and Tennessee, dotted as it was by Presbyterian churches. In many cases these records give invaluable material not only as to the date of settlements but also as to the racial complexion of their early inhabitants. A careful study of such sources may not show that certain types of soil and environment were peculiarly the choice of any one denominational sect, but factors of this character will be discovered of an exceedingly interesting nature.

For four years after the arrival of John Lewis, his wife, and three sons, the region remained "free" in the sense that all rights to land were to be secured only from the red men. Yet the Lewises were not without neighbors. The McDowells, ancestors of Governor McDowell of Virginia, Mrs. Thomas H. Benton, and the wife of President Taylor, came into Rockingham County about this time; the Campbells, whose great-grandson was to be the hero, one day, of Kings Mountain, came into the Tinkling Springs country a year after Lewis; and the Prestons, whose name is a part of Virginia's history, were also early arrivals. Among others were the Stuarts, from whom descended the famous cavalry leader, J. E. B. Stuart, the Buells, the Cochrans, the Tates, the Crawfords, the McCues (whose son John established the first Presbyterian church beyond the main Allegheny range at Lewisburg), the Hangars, the Mathews' (who were to give governors, later, to both Missouri and Georgia), the Porterfields, the McCulloughs and Zanes, names famous in Ohio Valley history. In large part these were all emigrants or sons and daughters of emigrants from Ireland (Ulster) who came up that long trail of the Shenandoah to occupy the table-land where that stream, the James, and the New arose.

Our purpose in giving in such detail the racial flavor of the Staunton settlement, is to bring out more clearly the fact of the definite change from German to Scotch-Irish, as Page and Rockingham counties were left in the valley and the highlands were reached; in a measure, therefore, we find that here, as was true in Pennsylvania, the inclination of the Scotch-Irish was ever to press on to the genuine frontier. Yet no absolute rule holds good; men of all races brought the best that their stocks had to give into this upland.

The whole problem of the patenting of the large tracts of land in this region and onward to Tennessee, Kentucky, and the Mississippi, calls for investigation; we know practically nothing of the data which led to the selecting of exact regions, and know in only a general way of the processes and purpose of the patentees or the terms upon which lands were sold. The Beverly Patent was issued on August 12, 1736, to William Beverly, who with his associates received 118,491 acres composing the "Beverly Manor." North of this patent Benjamin Burden of New Jersey (who became so well known on this frontier that the phrase "good as Ben Burden's bill" gave the same standard as that ascribed of old to the sterling by the Easterlings) received a five-hundred-thousand-acre grant. To the west, in the rich Greenbrier Valley which he discovered, John Lewis soon secured a grant of one hundred thousand acres. To the south, along the pathway to Draper's Meadows (Radford, Virginia), James Patton secured a grant of one hundred and twenty thousand acres. While in the distance, north of the North Carolina line (wherever that was), the Loyal Land Company had received its grant of eight hundred thousand acres. All of these grants came within two decades of the arrival of John Lewis at

Tinkling Springs, and they show the tremendous interest in speculation in lands which, a decade earlier, seemed as distant as the
moon to the average man. The sudden awakening seems to have
been due to the Hite-Lewis migration across the Potomac, and the
instant discovery of what a delightful land it was to which that
winding blue grass trail led.

So it is seen that there were great landholders here in the Highlands beyond old Frederick. No longer did the old Virginia "corn
rights" (one hundred acres for every acre planted in corn) or
"tomahawk claims" (blazing a line around a piece of land and
securing a patent to it) or "cabin rights" (securing forty acres for
building a cabin) hold good except outside these patents and on
land which the Indian had quitted. Close study in any specific
region should show interesting growths of settlements according to
these old laws—just over the patented lines.

But not one of the Carters or Burdens or Pattons or Lewises
or Beverlys was a Lord Fairfax. In contrast to his twenty shillings
per hundred acres a year rental (on a ninety-nine-year lease of
cleared land) the Beverly agents, for instance, asked only one
shilling per fifty acres payable annually on the feast of St. Michael
the Archangel. They required that three acres out of every fifty
should be improved each year; if the purchaser fell three years in
arrears in rental, or failed to improve the required amount, his
lease lapsed. Lord Fairfax was compelled to compete with these
upland grants at their price for unused land.

The development of these Presbyterian districts offers one of
the most interesting subjects the American history student can
find. Although the "Lord of the Hills" was having services
preached in his home by an ordained minister (James Thompson)
in 1739, within ten years the colonists of this upland were seeking
closer connection by road with the tidewater region of Virginia.
When this road was to be opened toward Goochland, the work
began with a prayer by John Lewis. The firm religious convictions
of these stern Calvinists shine out in their every act, public and
private, in contrast with what the Presbyterians were wont to
decry as the formality and indifference of the people of the Established Church in lower Virginia.

Stern were those Scotch laws when local government was established here. Local government of this kind in Virginia could only be formed by a vestry, a term not admired, we may be sure, by these lovers of John Knox; but they bent the neck willingly when a company of grim Presbyterians met, vestrywise, to officiate in the newly created county of Augusta! True to their Scotch principles of religion and education, Augusta Academy arose in the wilderness about Lexington in 1749; and later became Washington and Lee University.

Old World practices clung to these stalwart men, as seen for instance in the custom of "hating a man out" of the community who proved undesirable; with a conscience as tender as that of the orthodox Congregationalists in New England (from which numerous Scotch-Irish were "hated out" in earlier years) these devout Presbyterians haled men before the church on all occasions —Owen Crawford for drinking King James's health but refusing to drink to King George's; women for refusing to pay fines for sad crimes; Jacob Conger for driving his hogs over the Blue Ridge on the Sabbath day; James Frame for traveling ten miles unnecessarily on that day.

The local court partook of the same spirit of intense personal responsibility; it was tremendously incensed when the good wife of a certain citizen came into court "and abused William Wilson Gent, a justice, by calling him a rogue and that on his coming off the bench she would give it to him like the Devil"; it fined Joseph Tees twenty shillings for saying he "got nothing in this court but shuffling" and Francis Furguson for damning Governor Dinwiddie for a "Scotch peddling ——" and Charles Dever for cursing God.

In its splendid prosperity the region was as marked as was its type of religious independence. The vestry, assiduously performing its serious business, dealt with an astonishingly prosperous people; as early as 1747 there were 1,670 tithables in the parish and a population of possibly eight thousand people; yet the vestry had to report that the fund for the poor was intact, "the poor not being as yet known." When it is recalled that this region was, as the bird flies (and much farther by road), at a greater distance

from Philadelphia than the spot in the "far West" where Braddock would be defeated only eight years later, and that Philadelphia was the port through which most of Augusta's inhabitants
had come, the fact that they found no one who could be called
"poor" is significant.

This very fact of distance accentuated every element of independence and passion for separatism that was bred in the Scotch
character. The soils, lying on limestone and slate, made possible
an agricultural development wholly to their liking. It was excellent
for diversified farming and ideal for cattle raising because of the
small amount of undergrowth in the forests.

Here, where not a drop of water lies anywhere on the surface for a
moment after it falls [writes the historian of a neighboring county],
the foot and the sides and the tops of the hills, over hundreds of acres,
whether cleared or in wood—all parts seem alike fertile and verdant. At
the top no less than at the base does the timothy flourish until eaten
out by the yet more nutritious and fattening blue grass, which takes
final possession; and such seems to be the nature of all this region—
with this distinction, that where the oak is the principal growth, there
the land is more gravelly, throws up an undergrowth of wood, and is
better adapted for grain; while the prevalence of the maple, buckeye
and walnut shows more fitness for grass, and, like the blue grass of
Kentucky, is clear of undergrowth.[1]

Two other factors which make the study of the Staunton
region of unusual interest should be touched upon. One is the
independence which its geographical position far from the centers
of political control fostered; the second is the fact that its people
were of the kind to make the most of this. While no break took
place between them and the organized government of the colony
in which they were located, they interpreted its laws in their own
fashion and resisted sternly the gathering of illegal taxes or any
taxes which they believed were being collected by unscrupulous
agents. The records bear witness to the difficulty found in serving
writs in this highland, such as the suggestive one which states that
a writ was not served "because of an ax."

The colonial governments found the same awkwardness in exert-

---

[1] Dodge, *West Virginia*, p. 49.

ing long-distance control on this highland region that England had found when her colonists were located across the sea from her. And with every mile which increased this distance the difficulty seems to have doubled. Much of the diffidence in regard to the colonial problem of 1775 which is said to have marked these inland regions may be explained by the feeling of hostility which had grown up between the people there and the tidewater governments. The former suffered "taxation without [proper] representation" long before that became a battle cry—for as we have seen the property interests of the lowland plantations had warned the "rings" in control of legislation not to allow fair representation according to population to the hinterlands.

As the sweep of migration advanced beyond the Staunton zone this predilection for complete independence becomes plainer, until such a thing as a free state, the "State of Franklin," on the heads of the Tennessee was proposed, and a purchase of lands in far-off Kentucky was made in nonchalant defiance of Virginia law.

The other factor worthy of special note in connection with the Staunton zone is that the settlements here, their virility and prosperity, vitally affected a further advance along this historic track. As old Frederick in no small way was an outfitting post and starting point for Staunton, 135 miles away, so Staunton served a similar purpose for those who cared to push on to the James at what is now Buchanan, Virginia, or even farther to the New River at Radnor, Virginia.

Only prosperity, as we have seen in Pennsylvania, could make a settlement fitted to serve this purpose of helping to project a great movement. Such a prosperous island or oasis of population as Staunton could, and did, serve this purpose excellently, paving the way toward the Tennessee and Mississippi.

Chapter XIX

THE CONQUEST OF THE ALLEGHENIES

No one who has gazed across the splendid blue grass meadows of Montgomery County, Virginia, in the region about Blacksburg, where Virginia has located her State Agricultural College, will wonder why James Patton and the Loyal Land Company were led to look beyond Staunton for good lands.

As was the case with Staunton, so again here, we have no clear light on the early phases of discovery; a service can be rendered to Virginia history by those who can work this out, especially the early history of Pattonsburg on the James where the proprietor of this region lived as early as 1744.

Already the pathway from Staunton to Lexington and the James must have been well worn, for it is treated as a commonplace thing that George Draper, who had dwelt on the Schuylkill near Philadelphia since coming from Ireland in 1729, should push on with his wife and two children to Pattonsburg as early as the date mentioned, 1744. Over the divide, across the heights of Roanoke County, lay the magnificent meadows about Blacksburg, and beyond lay the fertile valley of the New River. Along the trail to this perfect country Dr. Thomas Walker soon fared to explore the lands of the Loyal Land Company; perhaps Draper and others went with him to the New River at this time.

At any rate upon the return of Walker in 1749 a considerable company was ready to take up land from the Loyal Company, and Thomas Inglis, a Scotch-Irish pioneer from Pennsylvania (a widower with three sons), Mrs. Draper, now a widow, with a son and a daughter, Adam Harmon, Henry Lenard, and James Burke crossed over the divide between the James and the New, and planted the first English settlement in the Mississippi Basin on the famed "Draper's Meadows" near Radford, Virginia. That they followed a well-worn trail, and left it a plain wagon road, is evident from the journal kept by Thomas Walker who came this

way a year later (in December, 1749); for he states that he "took
the main waggon road leading to New River."

Mr. Inglis married Mrs. Draper in 1750 and their plantation
at Draper's Meadows became at once a Mecca, as well as an
entrepôt, for some of the most important exploratory expeditions
in early western history. Not the least significant of these was
the forced migration of this heroine of the far frontier, Mary
Draper Inglis, into the heart of what is now Ohio (when taken
captive by the Indians the day before Braddock's defeat) on the
richness of whose soils she made full report after her escape.[1]

The rush of migration up this pathway from Staunton in the
years from 1750 to 1775 was unprecedented. It has been generally
treated by many writers; what is needed now is its careful study
in detail, paying attention to the earliest surveys, the allocation of
the grants and patents issued, the church and county records
which will give the racial characteristics of the settlers, the political practices instituted—all the ways in which the exigencies of
frontier conditions were met. The relations which were maintained
with the various outfitting stations located on the backward trail
to Staunton and Winchester and far-away Lancaster should also
be made more plain.

These pioneers scattered throughout the rich valleys in every
direction. James Burke found "Burke's Garden" in 1754 in Taz-
well County; Back Creek in Pulaski County was soon occupied;
the Reeds settled at Dublin and the McCorkles in Dunkard's
Bottom; others crept over the divide between the heads of the
New and the tributaries of the Tennessee on Cripple Creek in
Wythe County, and on to the headwaters of the Holston in Smythe
County. The writer has never enjoyed any exploration in any
county more than in finding his way across this ancient track from
the New River to the Holston through Max Meadows and Rural
Retreat. In imagination one meets the Boones trekking from
Berks County, Pennsylvania, to their future home on the Yadkin
before the young Boone started on his more famous adventures;
he passes the "Long Hunters" who, in 1770, did so much to bring
back from the far Cumberland River the tales which set this

---

[1] A. B. Hulbert, *The Ohio River*, chap. iv.

region aflame for further migration; he sees the Bullitt party of 1773 go by, and the Floyd party of the year after—the men who laid the foundations of the first temporary settlements in Kentucky; he meets the Chiswells who opened the lead mines in 1758, the McGarock family who came to Fort Chiswell in 1770, and the successor of Colonel Chiswell, Stephen Austin, who founded Austinville at the lead mines opened by Chiswell; and he sees the younger Austin go forth from these highlands to become the founder of the capital city of distant Texas.

The story of this river region, well called the "Sapphire Country," for the decade 1760–70, has been told only in terms of exploration by the Walkers, Boones, Smiths, Callaways, Carters, and others of lesser note. But as to colonization and settlement we are uninformed; yet when William Bean came into the historic Watauga Valley in 1769 he reported that there was a cabin on every desirable site along the Holston Valley, and ten families already settled along the Watauga.

To get the true picture of this migration one must note carefully the position of the present Elizabethton, Tennessee. Here later arose Fort Watauga. From the north comes the trail from Staunton and Draper's Meadows. From the east comes the trail from Charleston, South Carolina, a famous old route, which became a veritable highway when the South struck her stride in the next century. Over this "Rutherfordton Trace" came the early hunters who made known the Sapphire Country, along the general alignment of the Southern Railway by way of Saluda Gap and the Ashville region.

The historian of this route will do well to study the relationship which existed between Charleston and Philadelphia, for many of the Scotch-Irish who were to enter this upland chose the sea route from Pennsylvania and tracked northward from Charleston. Many came directly from Ireland to Charleston, as did the father of Andrew Jackson. Propaganda which was spread abroad by the first prospectors in the Sapphire Country and which helped to make Charleston the important port it came to be, would be an interesting subject for study, especially since with the coming of the Revolution thousands who previously had not perhaps thought of migration, were induced to do so because of British activities in the Carolinas.

Another interesting and vitally important phase of the history of this Watauga region which needs clear exposition is the boundary line dispute between Virginia, North Carolina, and the new state of Tennessee. The Virginia line had been run in 1749 by the noted surveyors, Joshua Fry and Peter Jefferson, only to the mountain range which became the western boundary of North Carolina. The ownership of these splendidly fruitful valleys of the Holston, Watauga, Clinch, French Broad, Nolichucky, and other rivers was, therefore, a matter under hot discussion, although by the Treaty of Lochaber (1770) they had been acknowledged as belonging still to the Cherokees! North Carolina had nothing to lose and everything to gain by not claiming the rich Watauga Valley, now soon to see a colony (the Watauga Association) as famous for intrepidity and stalwart personnel as either Draper's Meadows or Staunton. This fertile valley was in what North Carolinians considered their colony; but by not claiming it, offense toward the Cherokees in the valleys of the Tennessee was avoided.

While George A. Selwyn in 1766 secured a grant from the Crown to the pea-vine region of old Mechlenburg County between the Yadkin and Catawba rivers on the great route northward, the lands in the limestone valleys higher up had to be secured from the Indians. Goods such as clothing and cheap jewelry were so alluring that the red men decided on the policy of granting temporary leases. James Robertson, of Virginian ancestry, whose parents had lately moved into Wake County, North Carolina, got a lease of all the land on the Watauga for eight years for between five and six thousand dollars worth of merchandise. He had picked out the land while on a hunting trip over Daniel Boone's trace in 1770. He saw its value at a glance, and it became, as he anticipated, the butter and cream region of the South. Jacob Brown at the same time obtained a lease to lands on the Nolichucky.

The occupation of these zones marked by Mechlenburg, Watauga, and the Holston Valley between 1769 and 1772, shows an extraordinary admixture of the New England compact system, and the individual initiative system inspired by Virginia's allowance of freedom of locations. The factors of soil and climate, together with favorable vegetation were, however, dominant. The blue grass "balds" formed fine feeding grounds for cattle. The valleys furnished perfect soil for corn and wheat, and the forests provided provision for that mainstay of the grand advance, the razorback hog.

The porker should have been given his due credit earlier, for without taking him into account no one could properly describe the process of this colonization movement. Shaped like a thin wedge, so that lowland thickets had no terrors for him, with a snout as if made of metal, with long legs and thin flanks, this beast could "run like a deer and climb like a goat." According to Kephart, he outranked all beasts in courage and sagacity; was both a warrior and a strategist; he had a mind of his own and a fine understanding of human speech, especially profane speech. He could brood over indignities and bear grudges. As to these mental qualities, we must leave that to the Kephart school of psychologists, but as to the important fact that no other animal would take on one hundred and fifty pounds in eight months there can be no dispute. Such a prolific supply of healthy meat as the hog afforded in this far-distant highland should be considered one of the real assets of its occupation.

The splendid climate of the Sapphire Country made fruit growing as notable a factor as its cattle and its droves of swine. Its "Ben Davis," "Winesap," "Pippin," and "Lady" apples soon became famous. It is a quite significant fact that the planting of seeds or peach stones which would produce apples or peaches was commonly practiced in order to claim a title to land under the "tomahawk claim" system; by such planting was the first claim to Kentucky soil made.[2]

The political character of these Sapphire Country settlements and their governmental activities have been treated by several writers. They are among the most interesting in the history of our country. Much still needs to be done, however, in solving the rela-

[2] See pp. 184 ff.

View from the Summit of Grandfather's Mountain, North Carolina

tionship of the Watauga Association to the existing colonies, as well as to the Indians.

The independence bred by separation and the lack of long-distance control, which was mentioned previously, is well illustrated in Watauga. Its "Association" is an Appalachian type of the New England town meeting. The main reason for a local government here on the Watauga was the need of recording deeds to land. When Robertson and his fellow pioneers realized that the valley was south of the Virginia line, they felt that they owed no allegiance to the Old Dominion; being unable to render such to North Carolina there was nothing else to do but look upon themselves as an independent people. Accordingly in 1772 a legislature of thirteen was chosen by a general convention (a town meeting), and five commissioners were appointed to act in an executive and judicial capacity. Only the finding of the lost records of this first independent community in our American "West" will make possible the complete telling of one of the most interesting political incidents in our story of liberty. The names of many of these stalwart "Gods of the Mountains" are lost; but the roll of honor included the Carters, Robertsons, Smiths, Browns, Beans, Isbells, Seviers, Joneses, Russells, Womacks, Lucas'. The list is not, however, a more significant fact than that of the 113 signers of the Watauga Association in 1772, all but two could write their names. One wonders if this record could have been bettered by the first 113 pioneers to enter the Connecticut Valley from Massachusetts Bay?

Much has been written of the religious character of this Watauga colony but fresh light could doubtless be thrown on it by more careful study of church records. The strength of Presbyterianism shines out nowhere as a factor in government and education more clearly than in this region. The district made an abortive effort to create itself into a "State of Franklin" in 1784; the Houston Constitution (which was voted down by only a small majority in favor of the North Carolina Constitution) would in many essentials have delighted the hearts of Thomas Hooker, Cotton Mather, and all modern fundamentalists. Any citizen who by word or deed denied either the existence of one living and true

God, or the existence of a future state of reward and punishment, or who held that the Scriptures were not a divine revelation, or who denied the doctrine of the Trinity, was to be severely punished. Certain provisions of this trans-Allegheny law would be loudly approved today, such as the freedom of the press, which, however, provided that the authorship of all contributions must be made plain. It established a state university and a grammar school in each county. Yet at the same time it called for imprisonment for debt and a property requirement of each state legislator.

Thus, from the standpoint of the political influences of environment, this highest settlement on the limestone trail from Pennsylvania to Tennessee and Kentucky is by far the most interesting, especially in the quality of its democracy as illustrated in the articles of the Watauga Association and in this attempt to form the "State of Franklin" in 1784. It is a long journey from Sycamore Shoals to Plymouth Meadows beside the Connecticut. Yet in a sense that was the pathway traveled by the spirit of American democracy. And on that journey it was refined. In the "Fundamental Orders" proclaimed by those first pioneers who migrated over the Old Bay Path to Hartford, there is the spirit of the Englishman standing boldly for the best things for which the best men of their race had fought since Runnymede; in the articles of the Watauga Association there is the spirit of the American doctrine to be promulgated by hoarse muskets at Concord Bridge.

As Connecticut, our second frontier, was more liberal than Massachusetts, our first, so Watauga on her highlands was more liberal than Connecticut—at least in the significant particular of placing no restriction on the suffrage. It was Bancroft who said that these highlanders beside the Watauga and Holston "set to the people of America the example of erecting themselves into a state independent of the authority of the British King."

In primitive days when the only means of transportation were trails and canoes, the line of least resistance was always downstream. In the long trail of migration either from Philadelphia or Charleston to this highland region the course has been upstream.

But, once over the divide between the New and the Holston, the pathway is again downstream.

It is little wonder then that Watauga in its turn should become a rendezvous and outfitting post for a still further sweep of the Grand Advance; its limestone valleys were pathways leading toward the fertile oases of Tennessee, Kentucky, and the Mississippi Basin.

Chapter XX

THE BLUE GRASS REGION OF KENTUCKY AND BEYOND

THE central basin of limestone soils lying between the Ohio and Tennessee rivers is plainly marked on most maps.[1] Toward this basin trend all the limestone valleys from Pennsylvania, Virginia, North Carolina, and eastern Tennessee, along which marched the Grand Advance. Little did those plodding thousands seeking good lands, free lands, and escape from the tithe gatherer know the goal they or their children would find. They did not talk in terms of limestone or Hagerstown soils; indeed Joist Hite led the vanguard out on the long march seven years before Jonathan Hagar pitched upon "Hagar's Choice"; and Boone and many others had visited Kentucky long before Hagerstown, Maryland, was laid out in 1769.

But they did talk knowingly about the products of those soils, their grasses, flowers, shrubs, and trees. It gives a character to our knowledge and a background to our confidence to appreciate that while these tracking regiments seemed to be the victims of a *wanderlust* many other elements were involved; if it had been only *wanderlust,* there would have not been this planting of one zone beyond another, from Berkeley to Staunton, and Staunton to Draper's Meadows, and on to Watauga and Nashville, Tennessee, and Lexington, Kentucky, along one inevitable pathway of soil; if it had been that alone, this migration would not have shunned the short cuts to the Ohio Valley by way of the Great Kanawha gorges.

This fertile island of Hagerstown loam and clay soils lying in central Tennessee and Kentucky was, then, the actual goal of this movement; that it did not stop there is well known; but the pause in the movement at that point, and its occupation of the region, were so important politically that we are justified in calling it a

[1] *Ante,* chap. xvii.

goal. Kentucky is favored, judging by the reports of our Bureau of Soils, more than Tennessee in the distribution of these magnificent soils, having nearly a half million acres of the loam and clay practically evenly divided. Tennessee has a larger area of the loam (331,840 acres) but practically none of the clay. For diversified agriculture, therefore, Kentucky was the desirable land; its clay was one of the strongest soils for general agriculture, as well as for crops of wheat, corn, and grass in this country; from the loam come the important Burley tobacco crop and the blue grass which make this region famous.

How little attention has been paid to the relationship of these soils to early exploration of Kentucky, a glance at almost any authority will prove. The failures of the first explorers, Walker and Gist, to find the Blue Grass Region (so named from the bluish hue given to the landscape in summer by the seed vessels of the grass) has received hardly a comment from any writer so far as we know; the failure of Boone on his first adventures to reach and recognize the character of those soils and report the type of country is not commented on even by the chief authority on this nearer southwest. When it is considered that Kentucky was, supposedly, explored by both Walker and Gist in 1750, and that through the next two decades a large migration went into the Sapphire Country, it is a clear commentary on the general ignorance of the Kentucky land that no movement took place in that direction.

Walker only skirted the fertile region which he might have found; Gist never entered the supposed zone where the Ohio Company grant was made (between the Great Kanawha and Monongahela rivers). Walker could have engrossed the entire Blue Grass Region of Kentucky had he gone on to it; Gist doubtless knew the character of the Monongahela–Great Kanawha country he was sent to explore but he circled it, finally making a settlement at Mount Braddock in Pennsylvania, east of the Monongahela.

Dr. Walker's route for the Loyal Company is an interesting enigma. Getting into the "main waggon road leading to New River" he went to Inglis Ferry and then on over the road through Cumberland Gap which Boone was to follow for the Transylvania Company twenty-five years later. On the Cumberland River

near Barboursville, Kentucky (on the Faulkner farm), he erected
a house eight by twelve feet in measurement and planted peach
stone and corn, thus making "corn rights" and "cabin rights" for
his company. His bizarre voyage from that point can be explained
only by those who know the country and its ancient trails. After
floundering about the head of the Kentucky he went to Flat Top
Mountain in Raleigh County, West Virginia, and reached Staunton by way of Hinton and Hot Springs (where already six patients
were taking treatment!). All one can guess from his tour is that
he had acquired an inkling as to the rich region about Lexington,
but that in trying to reach it he was alarmed by the natives on
the head of the Kentucky, and returned the best way he could. His
report that he had found no good land was depressing.

Christopher Gist made his famous tour for the Ohio Company in this same year. He was ordered to go out and find lands
on the Ohio River and to go as far down as "the falls" (Louisville) if necessary; he was "to take an exact account of all the
large bodies of good level land," in order that the company might
make an intelligent location of the half million acres granted to
it. By the grant these were to be found between the Monongahela
and the Great Kanawha.

He explored the good land of central Ohio, then crossed the
Ohio at the mouth of the Scioto, entering Kentucky in Greenup
County, and went down toward "the falls." Warned away from
them by Indian tracks, he passed through Washington, Hamilton,
Nicholas, and Scott counties and came to the Kentucky River near
Frankfort, which he probably followed to the mouth of the Red
River. He then struck home through the rough region of Lee,
Perry, and Letcher counties and Pound Gap.

Gist thus missed the Blue Grass Region entirely, or at least
glimpsed it so little that its level character and wide extent made
no impression on him. Could he have realized that within a stone's
throw of his route lay the garden spot of the Middle West, and
had he so reported, it is conceivable that the whole episode of
the Old French War about Fort Duquesne might never have
ensued.

Difficulties of transportation played a part in hiding this most

CROSSING CUMBERLAND GAP INTO KENTUCKY

By permission, from *The Chronicles of America*

desirable portion of Kentucky from these and following adventurers—Colonel James Smith, John Findlay, and Daniel Boone (in his early voyaging). The Ohio River was a main line of entrance to this west on its northern border. The Warrior's Path through Cumberland Gap was the chief thoroughfare entering it from the south. This trail led quite directly to the mouth of the Scioto River on the Ohio, passing considerably to the eastward of the rich country about Lexington and Paris. The trail to the "falls" diverged from the Warrior's Path south of the Blue Grass Region, and passed to the westward of it, to the future site of Louisville on the Ohio.

The influence of the Cumberland River, which all hunting parties met as soon as Cumberland Gap was crossed, was also diverting. The famous "Long Hunters," as well as many others, followed the Cumberland and knew the country between the lower part of that river and the Green. As the Warrior's Path lay through rough country, while the branch which diverged toward the falls ran through a more level or rolling country to the south of the Kentucky River, "south of the Kentucky" became a watchword which told but half the truth. How much Daniel Boone, who hunted the country from his camp on Red River from 1769 to 1771, knew of what was to become the garden spot of Kentucky may never be known. When he left Kentucky in 1771, after twenty months of aimless rambling, in which he did not in the least seem to glimpse the importance of the future development of the Lexington country, great events were about to happen. That Daniel Boone was east of the Alleghenies during 1772, 1773, and 1774, will be emphasized by the student who cares to show who exerted the actual constructive forces in discovering the real Kentucky.

Col. William Preston of the famous Staunton family, was made surveyor-general of what is now Kentucky, and his deputies James Douglass, Hancock Taylor, and John Floyd, took up the work of surveying grants for numerous interests. Douglass knew the region, having visited the Big Bone Lick and probably other portions of the country in 1773. The principal work done by these men was in 1774, when they were recalled by the Governor who

sent Boone to warn them of the Indian war which was then break-
ing. These surveyors did real work in discovering Kentucky.
Douglass surveyed one thousand acres in Bourbon county for
James McDowell; he also surveyed land on Elkhorn, Hickman,
and Jessamine creeks; he pierced the heart of the rich Blue Grass
Region, knew Bourbon County and chose it as the site of his home.

The Finley and McAfee parties were surveying in Fleming and
Nicholas counties in this year, the latter covering the ground
where Frankfort now stands and also the valley of Salt Creek in
Mercer County above the mouth of Hammond's Creek. As Collins
epigrammatically observes, "Fayette County was thus 'surrounded'
—but probably not visited—by the whites, during that year
[1773]."[2] In Fayette County, which also lies in the richest blue
grass area, both Douglass and Taylor "surveyed many thousands
of acres" assisted by Isaac Hite; three thousand acres were surveyed for Henry Collins, two thousand for Alexander McKee,
and three thousand for Edward Ward. Taylor did surveying here
for other people at the same time. In this year John Floyd made
a survey for Patrick Henry on the Ohio opposite the mouth of
the Scioto River, and he made others in Kenton, Boone, Carroll,
Jefferson, and in the "elkhorn country"—now Scott, Fayette, and
Woodford counties.

The record of these surveys brings out the salient fact that in
1773 and 1774 the supremely fine lands of Kentucky were found.
Special pleaders for this cause or that, this settlement or that, are
inclined to slight the work of these pioneer surveyors who accomplished such constructive results. But for the breaking out
of war in 1774, they would doubtless have engrossed the best part
of Kentucky under the Virginia system. How this would have
worked out, so far as allowing the region to be exploited on a more
democratic plan, is a question open to debate. The author believes
that the best result possible was accomplished by war's interven-
tion at this moment; that Kentucky could not have become what
it was during the Revolution, nor have received the population it
did—which, after all, was the vitally important thing—if this work
under Colonel Preston had continued.

    [2] R. H. Collins, *History of Kentucky*, II, 176.

At the same time one should weigh properly the work of the men who labored here from 1772 to 1774. It was owing to them that Virginia and the whole country learned definitely of the great value of the Kentucky Blue Grass Region—and not to nomad hunters and Indian pursuers. As to the actual value of Kentucky lands, one word from Douglass or Floyd or Taylor or Isaac Hite, was worth more than a dozen from Daniel Boone; the latter was a master in path finding, but it is yet to be proved that he in any way assayed the relative value and productivity of Kentucky's soil provinces.

It would be difficult to overestimate the influence of the Blue Grass Region of Kentucky on American expansion and republic building. From 1775, when Boonesboro was planted on the Kentucky River by Boone for the Henderson Company, through the Revolution, Kentucky's population doubled each year. This swarming across the Cumberland Mountain barrier of so many bold frontiersmen, to exert a potential influence throughout the central Mississippi Valley, created alarm in Vincennes and Detroit, the nearest English outposts. The attacks upon the Kentucky stations, carried on or inspired from that quarter, led to Virginia's acquiescence in George Rogers Clark's belief in the necessity of the conquest of Kaskaskia and Vincennes as a military measure. It provided him with the means, and the campaigns of 1778-79 resulted in adding the "County of Illinois" to the Old Dominion.

It would be superfluous to discuss further Kentucky's soils in the face of the great body of literature on this subject; it is likely that popular knowledge of the soils and their influences in Kentucky is more widespread than is true of any other state, due to the works of Shaler, James Lane Allen, and John Fox. For the purpose of our study, however, something is gained by seeing clearly the diversified character of Kentucky's control upon migration in the decades following the Revolutionary War. Exact figures of the state's agricultural wealth in early days are not obtainable, but no state in the Union has maintained through the years so high a ranking in as many agricultural lines as Kentucky—in crops of tobacco, wheat, Indian corn, fruit, hay, and forage, and in herds of superior strains of cattle and horses. This diversity of produce is suggestive of a diversity of soils of uncommon virility.

The Blue Grass Region is a park bounded by a Highland Rim Plateau. Its richer portion, dominated by Lexington, occupies an irregular circle containing some eight hundred thousand acres. About this section lies a fringe and similar soil of like acreage, but a soil containing a smaller content of phosphorus and a larger quantity of sand. In the extreme southwestern corner of the state lies the "Black Patch" producing a heavy-leafed tobacco sold almost exclusively in Europe. Westward of the Blue Grass Region lie "the Barrens," known for their crops of Indian corn. Along Salt River in 1787 the first "Bourbon" whiskey was made from corn. All efforts in other states to manufacture whiskey from that grain never rivaled the Kentucky product, a fact explained by the character of the local limewater and yeast germs which gave an individuality to Kentucky corn. In the sandy, slaty, or cherty soils of the Highland Rim, or in the foothills of the Cumberlands, lie the farms of the less wealthy whites and the mountaineers.

To a very interesting degree, therefore, this first state west of the Alleghenies to be added to our Union (in 1792) may be said to have been "all things to all men." In the days of its growth and prestige—the four decades after its admission as a state—it offered to any agriculturist, cattle or horse breeder, almost any opportunity on any useful kind of soil that they could wish. It had homes for some of the wealthiest of American citizens and its proudest mountaineers were the poorest of the poor. The gradations between these extremes resembled the soil gradations. Kentucky drew most of its early population, and much of its later, from the South. Its aristocracy was wholly southern. Yet its democracy—represented by a surprising number of small farms —kept Kentucky from joining the South in Civil War days. Division of opinion on slavery (due to the inherited proclivities and prejudices of the original settlers and their descendants) and its abolishment, is significantly illustrated in the breaking up of the former large landholdings into small farms. In 1850 there were 74,000 farms in the state; in 1880, 166,000; in 1900, 234,000.

The importance of all this to us is that Kentucky contributed to the national migratory movement westward, an enormously valuable service throughout the half century from 1775 to 1825. Its pioneer population, as we have seen, necessitated the smothering of British-Indian activities in what became the county of Illinois after George Rogers Clark's campaign. A generation later, Kentucky's teeming population and large agricultural output was a factor (which the writer believes the most important single factor) in compelling the purchase of Louisiana. By the year 1800 there passed the revenue office at Fort Massac, Illinois, on the Ohio River, cargoes in flatboats to the value of $140,000 in the three months March, April, and May. In the three autumn months $32,000 worth and 24,500 weight of dry goods passed the same office. These cargoes included such items as 22,714 barrels of flour, 1,017 barrels of whiskey, 12,500 pounds of pork, 18,710 pounds of bacon, 75,814 pounds of cordage, 3,650 yards of country linen, 700 bottles, 700 barrels of potatoes. What proportion of this huge surplus (considering that the Ohio Valley had been but recently settled and that its pioneer population had, first, to be fed and clothed) came from Kentucky will never be known. Louisville, however, was made a port of entry in 1789 when the first revenue districts were established by Congress, and for ten years was the only American port outside of Atlantic waters. Whatever the proportion of this export wealth (which, reckoned in the purchasing power of money today, was very large) came from Kentucky, it formed Emerson's "dancing chorus of hope and promise" of great future prosperity. For many years, fifteen at least, the promoters of Kentucky agriculture had seen what Washington clearly foresaw in 1784—the absolute necessity of the economic waterway route to the Gulf of Mexico via the Ohio and Mississippi. Some of these men seem to have almost fulfilled Washington's prophecy that, if this natural export channel was closed to them, alienation of national affection was certain to follow. If this was rebellion, then the bursting of the chestnut burr is revolution and every winged maple seed is a rebel! The imperial integrity of those rich Kentucky soils was not to be defied.

Take for instance the case of such settlements on the Mississippi as Natchez. Its nearest source of supply in important agricultural lines was Kentucky. By 1803 the merchants of that city had contracted a $300,000 debt to Kentuckians and others, which they expected to pay in cotton. With the Mississippi closed to them (October, 1802) they were ruined, and their creditors bereft. Moreover, between 1800 and 1803, more than forty ocean-rigged sailing vessels had been built on the Ohio for foreign trade, of which Kentuckians had constructed many. Some of these sailed as far afield as Trieste at the head of the Adriatic.[3] The closing of the Mississippi meant disaster for capital invested in this enterprise. However much Jefferson's emissaries to Napoleon may have expected to purchase only the Isle of New Orleans, the West had, at least a year earlier, talked of the acquisition of all Louisiana, and western papers had cited fifteen millions as the purchase price, the exact sum to which Napoleon finally agreed.[4]

One great stream of immigration to Indiana and Illinois in these first years of the nineteenth century was through and from Kentucky, the Lincoln family being a typical case. The probable loss to the nation in the sale of western lands if the Mississippi was not (at least) internationalized was figured at $300,000,000. This was based on the assumption that: (1) 50,000,000 acres of western land would sink in price at least $2.00 per acre; (2) loss on land already sold on guarantee would be $10,000,000; (3) the total loss on 200,000,000 acres at $1.00 per acre would be that number of dollars.[5] But the purchase was made; the Mississippi ports were able to cancel their indebtedness to Kentuckians and others; and the sale of lands north of the Ohio to Lincolns and the rest far exceeded all estimates.

In the heyday of Kentucky's prosperity Henry Shreve solved the riddle of the western rivers. Raising the engine of the *Washington* out of the hold and putting it on deck, that mechanic defied the nautical wisdom of the day and made a steamboat which would sail on the water instead of in it. In eighteen years the

[3] A. B. Hulbert, "Western Shipbuilding," *American Historical Review*, XXI, No. 4 (July, 1916).

[4] *Pittsburgh Gazette,* April 9, 1802; the *Western Spy,* January 19, 1803.

[5] Senator Ross's speech in Congress, February 14, 1803.

steamboat tonnage of the Ohio and Mississippi rivers far exceeded that of the British Empire; it was 126,278 tons as against 82,696. The *Washington* and her successors made upstream navigation on western rivers successful. The great future and importance of the enormously rich valley of the Missouri River to its famous bend was now assured, and near the bend arose Westport (Kansas City), Independence, Leavenworth, Atchison, and Saint Joseph. In essentials it was as though a railway had suddenly been built between the fruitful agricultural regions dominated by Pittsburgh, Cincinnati, and Louisville (not overlooking the iron foundries of Pittsburgh) and the rich Missouri Valley. And at the bend diverged the trails which would put Oregon and California "on the map." The strength, virility, and wealth created by Kentucky blue grass soil was an important factor, perhaps the most important, in populating the Missouri Valley, just at the end of the profitable fur trade era, and rise of the steamboat era, and these men were to be concerned in the future occupation of Texas, Oregon, and California. Within these same strategic years, from 1818 to 1824, the Missouri Compromise determined the nation's slavery principles so far as they applied to the trans-Mississippi empire; and the government secured a right of way for the official survey of the ancient trail to Santa Fé and old Mexico.

How largely soil factors ruled as the main line of American migration went on, by water and by land, through Kentucky to the valley of the Missouri is evident. To dwell on the factor of soil attraction as we enter this Mississippi Valley phase of American expansion would involve a myriad of topics which can only be handled constructively by intensive local study. The field offers an amazing complexity of themes all of vital local significance. In so far as we have seen that local factors were inherently of important national concern historically, so the same types of factors in the western empire are of national consequence; as, for example, the exceedingly important relationship of agriculture to mining.

Space permits us to examine only major types of soil attraction and influence which ruled certain of the greater migrations from Missouri to Texas, Oregon, and California.

Chapter XXI

TYPES OF SOIL INFLUENCE IN THE WEST

LOOKING across the prairies and plains of the Great West, the many types of soil influences (and the collateral phases of American expansion to the Pacific coast which they suggest) quite defy description. Yet it is possible to make an outline classification of these factors to show their importance as well as the interesting ramifications of the theme. While no particular soil dominated migration in any such way as that in which limestone soils tended to facilitate the early drift of population from Pennsylvania and Virginia into the Old Southwest, yet an examination of many of the bizarre factors presented by the numerous soil provinces of the Far West will aid in the explanation of social and political developments. It is particularly true of this Great West that special pleaders have advanced many factors as " all powerful." Such propositions are difficult to establish scientifically as, for instance, one advocate of Sunday Schools as a *sine qua non* discovered; he held that "the most extensive influence" in awakening western migration was the promise of a certain organization that "within two years it would establish Sunday Schools in every destitute place where it is practicable throughout the Valley of the Mississippi."

Whatever classification is attempted with reference to any influence attributable to western soils, or whatever specific topic for investigation is undertaken, one broad and interesting theme always presents itself: men, singly, in twos or threes, or in masses, saw here a new world; they undertook life on new terms and found strange puzzles to master in soils and climates. All facts which develop these phases of experience are valuable; the record of mistakes made, lessons learned, handicaps overcome, and successes gained, is a real part of American history. It was only necessary, for instance, for the Kentuckian to cross the Ohio, as did Lincoln's father, and enter the prairies of Indiana and Illinois, to

encounter new systems of agricultural theory and practice. Here
topography offered to prospective immigrants a variation quite
unknown in many portions of the East. One of these variations
was that river valleys were, in effect, not valleys in the usual
sense. The typical river here constantly paved its immediate
"bottom" or land adjoining with a coating of rich soil whenever
its waters overflowed. Millions of small freshets or floods had so
coated the land near the streams on either hand, that the ground
there became more elevated than the surrounding lands farther
away; floods extending to these distant sections were less numerous and the rich loam was deposited there at less frequent intervals. Although this difference in elevation was slight, a matter of
even an inch influences water—and we have the curious historic
fact of George Rogers Clark's men wading for many miles through
the "Drowned Lands" of the Wabash. Such well-known *Guides*
for Eastern emigrants as Peck's, published in Boston,[1] forms an
interesting study of this phase of the psychology of migration,
for the mind of an emigrant acquainted with eastern swamps,
marshes, and quagmires, had to become readjusted to a "species
of inundated prairies" which "offered no inconvenience to the
people" if properly ditched.[2] The Atlantic seaboard swamp, with
its ten to twenty feet of muck, was rarely known in the plains
country; even "drowned lands" furnished fairly good footing for
Clark's men.

From another point of view eastern methods might be at fault.
Wet soils bred the frontier diseases of the fever and ague type,
and the inclination of strangers was to keep back from the immediate river shores in building homes. The theory was faulty
because germs in the air were more detrimental than those in
the water. The predilection of many newcomers for building
homes in retired nooks, vales, and coves, subjected them to living
on sites having poor air circulation; stagnant air eddies or pockets
proved more deleterious than water eddies, and often home sites
at a river's very edge were preferable because air circulation was
freer.[3] A traditional aversion to sites exposed to north or north-

[1] J. M. Peck, *A Guide for Emigrants* (1831).
[2] *Ibid.*, p. 94.   [3] *Ibid.*, p. 180.

west winds was also subject to valuable amendment here, on the
same score of healthful air circulation. Such winds in prairie lands
were "far less disagreeable than would be imagined"; artificial
windbreaks could be raised which, while mitigating the effects of
severe cold, yet permitted healthful circulation of air.

The topic of tree planting likewise introduces a theme on which
the "Down Easterner" needed information, since the average agriculturist, as has elsewhere been implied, could not conceive of a
treeless country as desirable. As a matter of fact actual absence
of trees was an almost unheard-of condition in the nearer West. On
the widest of Illinois prairies, timber was seldom more than five
miles distant from any emigrant trail; in most cases copses, groves,
and "points" of timber were frequently encountered and all water
courses provided some. Trees once planted, and preserved while
young, were likely to fare well; their growth proceeded at a rate
of which "no northern emigrant could have any just conception."[4]

All such phases of mental and physical adjustment of men to a
new environment, especially when applied to specific localities,
are interesting and valuable. For these data such books as Peck's
will be found useful. Moreover, similar guides and gazetteers appeared in considerable numbers throughout a long succession of
years; they portray, therefore, as no other media can, the developing stages of knowledge concerning the topography and
climatology of the West—the story of what men learned by experience as the struggle to overcome the handicaps of pioneering
went on. True, for some sections, even such media as mentioned
above will be found of small help. The case of California will
doubtless always remain the most striking illustration of confusion
as to early agricultural tradition; and data are extant to show
plainly how most previous experience had to be discarded in that
strange, new Pacific coast country.

Agriculture in California [wrote a frank old-timer] was the outgrowth
of hard-earned experience, and by unlearning most previous ideas and
disusing accustomed methods. The suburban farmer of Massachusetts
and of the Iowa prairies, were equally at fault. The agricultural books
and almanacs which said "This is the time to sow or plant" such and

4 J. M. Peck, *A Guide for Emigrants*, p. 119.

such seeds and roots, were utterly useless. The soil was different in different localities and required various methods of treatment. That chief implement of husbandry, the plow . . . underwent changes of structure consequent upon experiments and inventions suggested by the peculiar nature of the soil. The adaptive productions were not to be judged of by old rules. The richness of the soil, and the warmth of the climate, were no evidences that corn could be successfully cultivated; nor because wheat, oats and barley could be grown to advantage, was it to be inferred that potatoes and vines might flourish in the same vicinity. . . . the American farmer . . . learned, by trial, that irrigation was not necessary or desirable, for it caused the rootlets to sprout out near the surface; learned that the pulverized surface acted as an absorbent of the moisture from beneath; learned that the valley lands, where the first vineyards were planted, although they produce most luxuriantly, yet were inferior, for wine-producing qualities, to the hitherto neglected and dry hillsides; learned that even there irrigation could be dispensed with.[5]

Such detailed descriptions of homely, commonplace things, as soils and crops, are difficult to obtain. Many emigrants could not write; many who could were unable to find time to write. One source of information from those who could write and had time for it, as yet little explored, will be found in the reports and official and private letters of missionaries among the Indians. More widely than is supposed, testimony of this reliable type on the subject of future agriculture prospects was published in missionary papers and magazines and was copied in the secular press. It is difficult to emphasize how scarce in the early days was such information. In very many instances missionaries were country-bred men and women, acquainted with farming and farm economics. They could speak of soils, crops, and climates in many cases from personal experience. They were not financially interested in any project, and they were without doubt frequently idealists. Only the fur trappers and traders knew the early West better than the first missionaries. It matters not that few of the fur-trading profession could write; ignorant or skilled, they desired nothing so much as to keep the outer world in ignorance of the countries in which they hunted and trapped. Oddly enough,

[5] D. Chase, "Western Agricultural Improvements," *Overland Monthly*, IV (February, 1870), 149–151.

the best fur-bearing animals were normally to be found in the zones best fitted for agricultural development, as, for instance, the Bear River section of eastern Idaho. The trapper usually resented the coming of the missionary into his territory; partly, as is well recognized, because his influence was to make the Indian sedentary and agricultural; and partly, as is little realized, because the missionary was the forerunner of those who would be attracted to a fertile country by his reports. Agricultural development sometimes came so rapidly in the missionaries' wake that mission work itself was smothered, as in the case of the Willamette Valley missions in Oregon.

The reports of the Lees and others from the Willamette were published in full in such papers of wide circulation as the New York *Christian Advocate;* fifteen religious papers reprinted these accounts in full or in part and they were reproduced similarly in over ninety secular papers. These accounts helped to plant an agricultural section, which, because of its potential power, was a chief factor in aiding the United States to maintain successfully its claim to the 49th parallel as a Canadian–United States boundary line.[6] In the same country, to the eastward, the Whitmans and other American Board of Commissioners for Foreign Missions representatives gave the world much information concerning the fertility of the Columbia Basin. The very planting of their stations was wholly predicated by good soils.[7] After only two winters and an intervening summer in that field Dr. Whitman could write of the country:

. . . I think I can say it is as fine as one could desire. Our animals wintered in good order on the plains notwithstanding three of the cows had calves in the early part of the winter and one calf was even fat at the opening of the spring. I think we may expect good grass for cattle by the first of March . . . the country . . . I am satisfied will support a great population.[8]

One month after this letter was written the American Board was asked to send to Oregon thirty ordained ministers, thirty farmers,

[6] F. Merk, quoting Professor Turner, *Amer. Hist. Review,* XXIX, 690.

[7] M. Whitman to S. J. Parker, September 18; October 8, 1836. (MS Andover-Harvard Library.)

[8] Whitman to D. Greene, March 12, 1838.

thirty school-teachers, ten mechanics, and ten physicians, with their wives.[9] This order (which so staggered the reverend fathers in Boston) is of added interest from our point of view because it was inspired by a visit from Jason Lee on his way east, bringing out to the Willamette "the great reinforcement" which made that Methodist settlement so strong.

In the files and publications of a score of such missionary organizations (extending as far abroad as Germany) there lies a mass of data concerning the agricultural possibilities of many, if not most, of what are now the teeming farm regions of the West. The reports of Dunbar and Allis to the American Board from the rich Loup River section of the Platte drainage is an illustration in point. Such accounts tended to correct unfavorable impressions, which, as we shall see, were circulated even by scientific men concerning the "Great American Desert." The Methodist and American Board representatives in "Oregon" aided in counteracting some of the seemingly unfavorable ideas of the Columbia Valley expressed by Lewis and Clark. All who gave specific data of definite regions tended to aid in the establishment of a distinctly new agricultural theory concerning the West—the idea that productiveness of soil depended more on its physical characteristics than on its chemical composition. They gave men, as early as 1838, an inkling that despite seeming sterility soils produced definite crops according to climate and local conditions and that success depended largely in finding the proper crop for every soil—all of which illustrates the idea of imperial integrity suggested elsewhere. The antipathy of fur traders to missionaries forms a true criterion as to the missionaries' influence in making known to the nation its hidden corners. The sources which are here suggested for study provide ample proof of this fact. These sources are open today for study as they never were in the past; the great collections being made of religious periodicals and newspapers by such organizations as the American Antiquarian Society will prove helpful in the work.

The relationship of productive lands and soils to the establishment of the military keys of the West, its frontier forts and sta-

[9] Spalding and Whitman to Greene, April 21, 1838.

tions, particularly the stations on important lines of communications, may usefully be considered. In the confidential instructions issued by Gov. George Simpson to guide the secret reconnaissance of Warre and Vavasour in 1845 (preparatory to the possible military defense of England's claim to the Columbia Basin) we read:

> You will see from the extent of the [Hudsons Bay] Company's agricultural operations and from the large quantities of cattle and sheep at their establishments of Fort Vancouver, the Cowlitz and Puget Sound, that they could provide the means of subsistence for any naval or military force that is likely to be required in that quarter, and other parts west of the Mountains, while the Sturgeon, salmon, and other fisheries are inexhaustible.[10]

The statement suggests a review of the commonplace but vital topic of the agricultural background of western military history which has, naturally, been neglected for the more colorful story of martial and political events. This would give that comfortable sense of reasonableness to the location of such posts as Pierre, Leavenworth, Laramie, Kearny, Bent, Union, Cummings, Thorn, Camp Grant, and Yuma—the experimental nature of some, and their later abandonment. So patent a theme needs no elaboration, but there are less self-evident features of a similar character which investigation might reveal. There has never been, for instance, a satisfactory explanation of the government's refusal to pay the Bent Brothers the price asked for Fort Bent; the refusal led to a rather petulant destruction of the place by its owners. Would the records not show that such factors as those we have under review will explain the government's action? Was Fort Bent fitted for expansion into a great rendezvous—because of adjacent forage, water, and wood? Could the site, from these considerations, compare for a moment with that of Fort Union, later erected near by, where local conditions were very favorable? Again, the inability satisfactorily to supply the Forts Fetterman, Reno, and Smith, on the Bozeman Trail through northern Wyoming and southern Montana, compelled their abandonment. In turn this led, in 1862, to the abandonment of the entire line of the original Oregon Trail

[10] Public Record Office Files, "America Domestic Various," Vol. 440, May 30, 1845.

west of the Rockies in Wyoming—the North Platte–Sweetwater–
South Pass trail. Few prolific sources of information on any American topic have been so scantily used as the War Department records which contain so much of value relating to the pioneer West.
The history of planting, supplying, maintaining, or abandoning the
scattered military posts will be made more thoroughly understandable when these sources are more widely examined; doubtless
many phases of regional productiveness will be found to play an
unsuspected rôle when the full story is told.

As to western lines of communications, the domination exerted
by the three W's—wood, water, and wild grass—is well known. The
story of migration over the Oregon or Santa Fé trails was the story
of hurdling, so to speak, from oasis to oasis. When one uses the
term "trail," as in the preceding sentence, one should never understand the word to be synonomous with "track." In many isolated
instances topography compelled the use of one track for short
distances, as in Marshall's Pass at Scott's Bluffs on the Oregon
Trail in Nebraska. But for hundreds of miles these routes were
veritable ganglia of pathways. Sometimes these were feet apart;
sometimes rods; sometimes miles. Difficult topography in numerous cases dictated these lanes of travel, as, for instance, the fourteen known tracks down into Ash Hollow on the Oregon-Cali-
fornia trail. More frequently, however, the three W's broke the
trails into antennae reaching out across sand or rock or alkali for
water or for grass. Whenever any of these failed, that route fell
into disuse, temporary or permanent. The altering of conditions
which offered forage or water on the various lines of the old trails
explains the rise and decline of so many of the side trails and
parallel tracks.

An interesting illustration of this is afforded by "Ice Slough" on
the upper Sweetwater River in Wyoming. Many travelers even
earlier than the forty-niners, refer to the curious circumstance
of digging ice in July in this portion of the sun-parched desert of
the Sweetwater Valley. Later immigrants (after 1849) comment
with derisive sarcasm on all such statements of their predecessors;
they imply that the heat of the torrid region turned the heads of
such *raconteurs* and that the ice seen was only a mirage. Hewitt

in 1862, for instance, comments with hilarious mirth on the record of Delano of 1849. Both of these writers were conscientious, reliable men; both wrote truthfully of the same valley or slough in different years. The explanation of the discrepancy is very simple. An inland valley, perhaps thirty yards in depth and a hundred wide from crest to crest, is fed by several small living springs. In the old days strong grass grew high in this depression. In winter a solid coating of ice was formed on the surface and the tall dried grass formed a veritable thatched roof which preserved the ice as late as early July, for the nights at this altitude are cool even in midsummer. The great number of animals accompanying the forty-niners destroyed the grass in the Slough; later comers never found it of sufficient height and thickness to perform the old-time miracle. The explanation of this mystery solves more important matters than correcting the aspersion cast upon the reliability of the journals of the earlier immigrants, although that is a matter of no mean importance. The Slough explains the location here of the old pony express and overland stage station of Rongis and its passing.

In the whole question of relocating and identifying the historic sites of pony express and stage stations, factors like those presenting themselves at old Ice Slough need to be considered. While the spacing of these wilderness stops and relay posts was a matter of the length of "runs," they were dominated by supplies of water and forage; in all cases something of a compromise had to be effected. The alteration of many sloughs and little water courses by present-day irrigation projects, and the drying up of numerous springs, make this work of the historical allocation of the old trail stations difficult. Locally it is, however, a matter not without its importance; when correctly done it assumes a value to the world at large by making more intelligible the hundreds of overland diaries and journals which Americans will never wholly cease to read and admire.

If this is true of the old trails it is truer still, and more significant, when applied to early railway explorations, surveys, and location. As historical consciousness develops in the Far West to the degree long evident in the East, and lately in the Mississippi

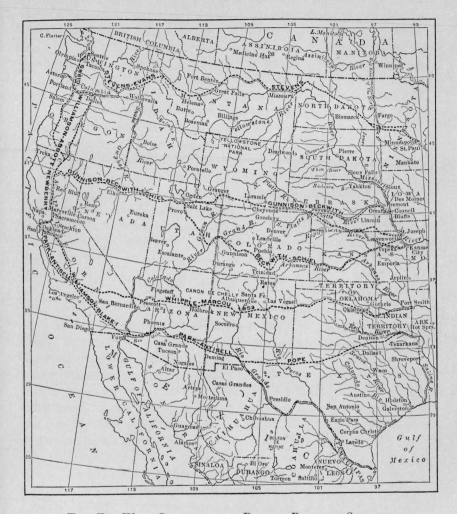

THE FAR WEST SHOWING THE PACIFIC RAILWAY SURVEYS

By permission, from *The First One Hundred Years of American Geology*, by George P. Merrill, published by Yale University Press

Basin, attention now paid to the romancers who wrote the lives of Calamity Jane, Jesse James, Billy the Kid, and others, whose contribution to the constructive building of the West was no greater than that of so many prairie dogs, will be given, it is hoped, to the splendid work of the Boones, Aberts, Emorys, Pecks, Marcys, Whipples, Parkes, Warrens, Mendalls, Williamsons, Beckwiths, Gunnisons, Popes, Beales, Bryans, Palmers, Stanburys, and Moores who gave the best of their lives (some of them life itself) to unravel the mysteries of mountain and desert in the cause of the traffic of civilization. Laboring through the early years under the artificial handicap—a veritable obsession—that such railway lines might follow parallels of latitude, these men and many others performed prodigies of toilsome and often fruitless exploration, some of which (but by no means all) is suggested in the series of giant tomes—*Pacific Railway Reports*.

When this truly heroic epoch comes to be studied scientifically, factors of soil and vegetation will be very usefully employed to interpret much which now passes as unexplained. Lines of parallels gave way to a serious consideration of the topographical lore of dividing ridges, and heads of rivers, as discussed in the opening chapters of this work; successive "islands" of favorable soil became connecting links of vast chains of iron rails which should bind the country together. These potentially productive oases would some day witness the planting of the farms and ranches, villages and towns, which would provide the railways with the sinews of strength—traffic. We rarely think of this great work of continental conquest being predicated by soils and vegetation, but the briefest glance at the Pacific Railway records mentioned above will show how many supplementary factors were consulted in the prospecting of transcontinental routes. Plats of lines were laid out in accordance with geology, climatology and flora, zoölogy and paleontology, mineralogy and hydrography—as well as agriculture. Astrology seems to have been about the only science of ancient fame that was not consulted when the West was being scrutinized for railway lines. One may survey, if one chooses, maps twenty feet in length showing in miniature every change in tree growth along the whole fifteen-hundred-mile stretch of a proposed railway—

each alteration indicative of soil changes, drainage changes, altitude variations, vegetation differences. There is more material of genuine romance in the discovery of Aubrey's Valley, as a lifesaving oasis on the pathway through arid Arizona which later became the route of the Santa Fé railway, than is contained in the whole life story of any bank or train bandit that ever lived. How dominant in all this blueprinting of the West for railways was the agricultural factor is made plain in any of the forty reports and reconnaissances.

From the end of the track at Sheridan [Kansas, wrote General W. J. Palmer to the Directors of the Union Pacific, concerning their proposed southwestern line] to the Arkansas at Fort Lyon, a distance of 120 miles, the country is adapted to grazing for migrating flocks and herds. . . . The valley of the Rio Grande, for 200 miles north and south of Albuquerque appears to be formed of a highly productive loam. Everything grows luxuriantly in this soil by irrigation. . . . Fifty miles west of the summit [Gallup, N.M.] we found the Zuni Indians cultivating the soil extensively without irrigation. . . . For the next 100 miles [Flagstaff, Arizona, region] we have the finest country met with, perhaps, on our entire route. Its soil, black and rich from the decomposition of lava, will produce without irrigation wheat, barley, oats and potatoes, in the heaviest crops. "It is the most beautiful region," wrote Beale, "I ever remember to have seen in any part of the world. . . . " The Valley of the Great Colorado is wide and fertile. Whipple pronounced the soil far superior to that of the Rio Grande. . . . The valley of the Mohave has a narrow fringe of rich soil that can be irrigated from the river; it is especially adapted, both from climate and soil to the culture of cotton. . . . Thence to San Francisco, about 300 miles, our route lies entirely through a productive country with splendid pasturage and good soil. [In the coast valleys of the] Salinas, Pajaro, San Juan and Santa Clara wheat and barley grow almost spontaneously, enabling the *mining state* of California, as we have seen in the past two years [1866–68] *to command the breadstuff markets of the world.*[11]

The many instances of arbitrary fixture boundaries in the happy-go-lucky way we chose to do such things in the West, as running of state lines, boundaries of Indian reservations, and even-

[11] *Report* (Philadelphia, 1869), 117 ff. Cf. J. S. Silver, "Farming Facts," *Overland Monthly*, I, 177.

and-odd allotment of sections to railways along their rights of way, will offer students of soil factors many curiosities of social and political disorder to unravel. For all such cases of forlorn isolation of rich provinces from their political centers, and the consequent hybrid affiliations formed with more adjacent sections, the study by the late Professor Bassett, elsewhere quoted,[12] will always form a kind of a model to be followed as circumstances permit. In this connection there is the topic (which itself is worthy of a volume by another Hinsdale or Treat) of the relationship of soil provinces to the work of surveying the national domain. This topic has been left untouched largely because so little information has yet been secured on the subject of American surveying. A field here is open for a book of as commanding importance as either *The National Land System* or *The Old Northwest*. The technicalities of the subject practically debar the historian from the task; it remains for the historically inclined civil engineer to undertake it. What a medley of systems it will be for him to unravel! Many lines, supposedly the same, run in opposite directions to the theoretical meeting point and never meet! These are compromised by convenient "jogs." In surveying across any large area of a round object, like our Earth, dressmakers' tucks had to be taken; this was done by dropping out of the picture whole tiers of townships. Emigrants actually bought land which existed on paper but not on land—not even "under water"! Strange results followed this jumbled method, such as Wisconsin's loss of Chicago. The rise and growth of such an association as The American Agricultural Society makes probable the depicting of the great need of work correlating soil questions to those of such importance as the history of surveying.[13]

[12] P. 37.

[13] The quarterly publication of this society, *Agricultural History*, is proving a valuable medium for development of topics within its scope. Those published in the three volumes issued which are of moment to this study on soils are as follows:

E. Merton Coulter, "The Movement for Agricultural Reorganization in the Cotton South during the Civil War," I, No. 1 (January, 1927), pp. 3–17.

C. A. Browne, "Some Historical Relations of Agriculture in the West Indies to That of the United States," I, No. 2 (July, 1927), pp. 23–33.

W. L. Westermann, "Egyptian Agricultural Labor under Ptolemy Philadelphus," I, No. 2 (July, 1927), pp. 34–47.

The development of the story of the surveying of the West will provide necessary data of a scientific character to show the process of the dissolving of the "Great American Desert" myth. With unbelievable persistence an erroneous impression was conveyed to the public on this score even by government employees of high scientific standing. As late as 1859 Professor Joseph Henry of the Smithsonian Institution was preaching in the columns of the *American Agriculturist* that "a vast extent of country, almost one half of the width of the American Continent was quite unfit for tillage." From the 98th meridian to the fertile Pacific coast val-

L. C. Gray, "The Market Surplus Problems of Colonial Tobacco," II, No. 1 (January, 1928), pp. 1–34.

B. T. Galloway, "Plant Pathology: A Review of the Development of the Science in the United States," II, No. 2 (April, 1928), pp. 49–60.

Ellen Churchill Semple, "Ancient Mediterranean Agriculture," II, Part I, No. 2 (April, 1928), pp. 61–98.

Claribel R. Barnett, "The Agricultural Museum; An Early American Agricultural Periodical," II, No. 2 (April, 1928), pp. 99–102.

Edmund C. Burnett, "The Continental Congress and Agricultural Supplies," II, No. 3 (July, 1928), pp. 111–128.

Ellen Churchill Semple, "Ancient Mediterranean Agriculture," II, Part II, No. 3 (July, 1928), pp. 129–156.

Edward Everett Dale, "Those Kansas Jayhawkers; A Study in Sectionalism," II, No. 4 (October, 1928), pp. 167–184.

Rodney H. True, "Jared Eliot, Minister, Physician, Farmer," II, No. 4 (October, 1928), pp. 185–212.

Waldemar Kaempffert, "The History of Agriculture and the Rosenwald Museum," II, No. 4 (October, 1928), pp. 213–214.

Arthur P. Whitaker, "The Spanish Contribution to American Agriculture," III, No. 1 (January, 1929), pp. 1–14.

Carl R. Woodward, "Agricultural Legislation in Colonial New Jersey," III, No. 1 (January, 1929), pp. 15–28.

Bernhard Ostrolenk, "The Henry C. Mercer Museum," III, No. 1 (January, 1929), pp. 29–32.

Earle D. Ross, "Lincoln and Agriculture," III, No. 2 (April, 1929), pp. 51–66.

St. George L. Sioussat, "The Breakdown of the Royal Management of Lands in the Southern Provinces, 1773–1775," III, No. 2 (April, 1929), pp. 67–98.

Ernest S. Osgood, "The Cattleman in the Agricultural History of the Northwest," III, No. 3 (July, 1929), pp. 117–130.

L. O. Howard, "The Rise of Applied Entomology in the United States," III, No. 3 (July, 1929), pp. 131–139.

E. Merton Coulter, "A Century of a Georgia Plantation," III, No. 4 (October, 1929), pp. 147–159.

R. H. Anderson, "Agriculture in the Museum of Science and Industry Founded by Julius Rosenwald," III, No. 4 (October, 1929), pp. 182–186.

leys, stated Professor Henry (except for "mountain valleys" about Great Salt Lake where irrigation afforded "a precarious supply of food" at the cost of privations "from which American citizens generally would shrink") lay "a wilderness unfitted for the uses of the husbandman." With typical eastern dogmatism, Professor Henry affirmed that when the facts were "fully appreciated," the knowledge would

serve to dissipate some of the dreams which have been considered as realities, as to the destiny of the western part of the North American continent. Truth, however, transcends even the laudable feelings of pride of country; and, in order properly to direct the policy of this great confederacy, it is necessary to be well acquainted with the theatre on which its future history is to be enacted, and by whose character it will mainly be shaped.[14]

The statement forms a good illustration of that self-satisfied type of "Yankee" thinking which Owen Wister described as "rancid with philanthropy and ignorance." Within four years D. S. Curtis was pointing out in the *Wisconsin Farmer* that the "apparent destitution of water" which made easterners lose faith in the future of western agriculture was "in some respects a blessing as it will induce or drive people to use water from the clouds rather than that from the earth"; thus as early as 1863 the whole reservoir and dry-farming theory of agriculture was being voiced distinctly.[15] Henry in 1859 stated that the plains could not support double the number of the scant flocks and herds then owned by the Indians living there; but as soon as 1866 an authority of note declared that that region would "become the greatest wool-producing country in the world."[16] It will doubtless appear when the proper research is made, and comparisons instituted, that it was the scores of reports made upon surveys for Pacific railways, like that of General Palmer's elsewhere quoted, which corrected false impressions concerning the plains and deserts, and stamped as legitimate the theory that all that was needed was to find the proper crop for every available soil.

[14] Quoted in *The California Culturist*, I (May, 1859), 503–506.
[15] Quoted in U.S. Department of Agriculture *Report for 1867*, pp. 230, 236.
[16] *Ibid., Report for 1866*, p. 130.

Unquestionably California will be recognized one day for an agricultural service of a value second only to the value of the mineral wealth which she bequeathed to the world. While Professor Henry doomed millions of western acres, which are now fruitful, to a sterile oblivion, he excepted, of course, the rich valleys of our present Pacific coast states. But California offered a practice-ground for agriculture of unequaled importance. In her vast area was found not only every rich and fruitful type of soil known anywhere in the West but also every drear and sterile type; and study will prove, that just as Californians took abroad—to Carson River, Frazier River, and "Cariboo"—lessons in the art and practice of mining and in mining legislation, so Californians put in practice in their infinite variety of soils and climates, theories of successful agriculture, and sent and carried those lessons eastward to the great arid regions between the Sierras and the 100th meridian. Such studies will show how California was an agricultural school for the men of the mythical Great American Desert. They will show with what earnestness—never surpassed by the "forty-niners" of the Sacramento Basin—Californians undertook the solving of the problems of their soil provinces, bewildering as these were in number, and in type, and in climates. You will look in vain in the agricultural annals of the time of many Atlantic seaboard states, for a record of efforts of such sterling scientific character as were put forth in the fifties by Californians to secure information about soils and methods of handling different soil types. For instance, in what eastern states were questionnaires being sent out this early that will compare with that issued by the California Agricultural Society in 1858 and which read:

1. What is your locality? mountain or valley, prairie or river bottom.
2. What is your climate? Snowy, frosty, foggy, dry or wet.
3. What were the native productions of the soil in your vicinity? in vegetables or minerals, either or both.
4. What is the character of your soil?
5. What is your method of cultivation?
6. What grains, grasses or fruits do you raise, and in what quantities?
7. What is your method of rearing and marketing your stock, poultry, etc.?

8. What vegetables flourish best on the different soils?

9. What fruits do you find best adapted to the different soils, as alkaline, loamy, sandy, clay, etc.?

10. What are the results of irrigation upon fruits, fruit trees, etc.?

11. What is your method of planting orchard trees—preparation of soil, size of hole, distance, with or without water?

12. What is your method of pruning and trimming the different kinds of trees, vines and shrubs?

13. How do your productions compare, in quantity and quality, with those of the same varieties raised in the Atlantic States or Europe?

14. What growth do your fruit and ornamental trees make, as compared with the same time and varieties elsewhere?

15. What prices do the different kinds of fruits bear in your vicinity?

16. What diseases or insects infest fruits and fruit trees in your vicinity, and what remedies are applied?

17. What is the most approved method of packing or putting up grapes and other fruits to preserve in their natural state for winter use?

18. What is the best method of putting up peaches and other fruits, IN CANS, to keep fresh?

19. What is the best method of ripening winter pears, apples, etc.?

20. What (in detail) is the best method of making the different varieties of wine?

21. A communication upon any one or all of these points will be gratefully received and tend to advance the interests of our whole people.

Not only did California have a greater number of soil series than any other American commonwealth, but it had variations in climates and floristic zones not known elsewhere. Some of these variations were as baffling (in their reactions to culture) as the tricks of any magician; the seeds of a black grape from Los Angeles transported to the Sacramento Valley produced a white grape; and the first (red) apple seeds brought from England to our Pacific Slope produced a tree which bore a colorless apple its first year but, on thinking it over, produced red ones ever after![17] Research would doubtless show that not a "mountain or valley, prairie or river bottom" soil, nor a "snowy, frosty, foggy, dry or wet" climate between the Kansas and Nebraska uplands and the Sierras, but profited in some way in later days from successes

[17] H. H. Bancroft, *Works*, XXVIII, 441, n.

first achieved in California. Proofs of this are to be found in the use of California agricultural literature in those sections.

Our effort has been to show types of soil influences, and therefore types of soil studies to be made in various scattered sections of the trans-Mississippi West. Our only hope was to be suggestive. In closing, a topic may be mentioned of general interest not only to all that region, but to the country at large as well—the study of the rise and spread of agricultural journalism and the side lights on our main theme which investigation may throw. Beginning with the first agricultural paper in our country, founded at Baltimore in 1819, the western extension of such efforts is not without significance. Papers of this type issued at Germantown and Albany would be third on the list in order of publication, ignoring duplications. The *Prairie Farmer* of Chicago would rank seventh, the *Southern Cultivator* of Athens, Georgia, ninth, and the *Wisconsin Farmer* and *Coleman's Rural World* of St. Louis would tie for twelfth place. These both appeared in 1849. The *California Farmer* was established in 1853, only one year later than the famous *Ohio Farmer;* and the *Iowa Homestead* of 1856 antedated by one year the *Rural American* of New York City. Only twenty agricultural papers had been published in the United States when the former journal was founded in Iowa. For the agricultural historian there is being gathered in many storehouses—notably such new and significant ones specializing in this theme as the McCormick Agricultural Library of Chicago—an enormous mass of the material conserved in such sources.

A NEW BASIS FOR THE STUDY OF
LOCAL HISTORY

THERE is perhaps no town, township, or county in the United States which could not be taken as a concrete subject for a study of local history of a new type, and the field ought to be particularly attractive to patriotic organizations sometimes at a loss to find interesting subjects to develop, and to all out-of-door clubs and leagues of young people. Phases of the subject are worthy of graduate study, particularly those relating to the history of American surveys.

It is true that there are such patent diversifications of topography that subdivisions of any theme might be necessary. But whether one chooses the whole or a fraction of any section the method of procedure would not differ very greatly. In the first place it is necessary to banish from one's mind the idea that the history of any such section is trivial or commonplace. Any county in America has an interesting background. It "grew up" from unknown beginnings to its present estate. We must see that growing-up process. Here recourse will be had to the "handmaiden" science of geology. This field, of course, has by no means been neglected, but the methods of presentation have often been too scientific—too much a matter of confusing words which the uninitiated hardly master—to produce practical results. In coöperation with local and state authorities, simple key models should be made showing the stages of a county's growth throughout its geological history. These "keys" prove, upon completion, to be of very genuine popular interest; the "birth" of this mountain range, that mesa, this river valley, or that range of hills, comes to be—when seen in proper perspective—an exciting thing. One gets from such a moving picture a concrete sense of development; acquires a new kind of confidence. Reasons appear to explain things which once just seemed to have "happened"; principles are, in a sense, created before your eyes, which make you realize the integrity of any given locality. You then discover the basis for knowing why your given country produces corn, vineyards, Aroostook potatoes, beet sugar, mills, factories, cities. By comparing the models—or charts, it may be—one is impressed with the sense of the mighty, continuous processes that never cease; one gets the thrill which accompanies the knowledge that New York City is today sinking into the Atlantic Ocean just as fast and just as surely as, one day, the Rocky Mountains rose.

Topographical key maps of the section under survey should now be made and all the material suggested in our chapters on waterways and river controls in relation to the main watershed is to be analyzed. So far as state geological maps or the topographical sheets of the United States Geological Survey are obtainable they will be found essential. If not obtainable for your section those of other sections should be used as models. With the framework of a county thus platted the "handmaidens" of history may be called upon to aid in filling in the details—forestry, climatology, botany, zoölogy, mineralogy, and agriculture. The forested sections should be mapped as fully as possible from any data that can be secured; if the entire region was forested, pioneer accounts will be likely to show where glades, savannahs, or prairies existed. With the help of the zoölogist the region should be shown to have been the habitat of some of the heavy game animals, although any fur-bearing animal influenced the first social movement, for it brought the trapper and trader. The story of the heavy game animals is important because of the paths and runways which they broke open. This introduces the important subject of watersheds and dividing ridges, correlating itself with your maps already made showing drainage systems. Frequently one need not ask concerning main watersheds, for mountain chains proclaim this fact. Very often, however, where significant ranges do not exist, this becomes an interesting theme; and curiously enough, in supposedly "dead level" prairie countries it is of greater interest than ever. Maps should be made to show the longest ridges running across the county or interlocking among themselves within its limits. Special attention to these highland maps will give the student most interesting results. Here lay the county's first trails.

Forest growths here were lighter; winds that swept these heights kept the trails freer of snow in winter and of wind rack the whole year round. Paths here were lifted out of the soft earth of the valleys, giving all animals surer footing. If in your country the earliest Americans, the mound-building Indians, had their homes, these highland routes were their pathways for all overland travel, and through the United States Bureau of Ethnology reports (if not from reports of your State Historical Society) you can secure data as to the location in your region of the archaeological remains (earth- or stoneworks) left by the "oldest settlers." The highest ways of your county are probably marked here and there by stone cairns of those first Americans. If such data exists it should be incorporated on the maps of your highland routes.

Problems will be faced when this matter of primeval routing is gone into in detail. Main thoroughfares, almost as old as the hills themselves, will be found on the great dividing ridges. But main routes will also be found along those natural pathways, the river valleys. In many cases no watershed will exist all the way across a county. Animals were compelled, then, to descend into valleys, and strike up other ridges. The identification of the old crossing places of rivers will prove of assistance in checking these lines. Curiously enough, a single fact mentioned elsewhere in this volume, if remembered, will be of help here: The first red or white men in any section were likely to cross streams where animals had been accustomed to cross, for animal paths were those used by men. In more than 50 per cent of all such cases the later white men's ferries over streams of any width were located at these points— just above or below the old-time ford. The examination of the volumes giving the first statutes of any state will show where the first ferries were authorized. It was usually the rule to ford streams below the mouth of important tributaries; for the freshets from the incoming stream brought supplies of silt which formed islands in the larger stream. Railways in a later century often made use of these island formations to bridge streams at such points. On the key maps showing a county's early thoroughfares all points where early legislation showed that the first ferries were established may be tentatively marked as prehistoric fords.

Another check of like character can sometimes be made of the alignment of the chief highland routes. Very frequently where a railway tunnel exists you will find, just above it, the most important ancient route of that particular district. Where several railway tunnels are met with in succession, the same prehistoric thoroughfare may be found over each. The unerring tripod in later times picked out those tunnel sites as the most strategic in passing from one river source to another. The instinct of the deer, moose, or buffalo in earlier centuries discovered that same truth, and their path above the tunnel attests the fact. While drawing in the prehistoric routes it must be remembered that white men's early routes followed those of the red men, and that the latter followed to a considerable degree those of animals. It is well then, in this connection, to make a study of the historic trails first platted by the original surveyors of each township in every county which we shall describe below.

By our plan then we now have in hand key models, or charts, showing the geological growth of a county. By another series of charts we have depicted the topography of the same county; and superimposed upon these (or drawn on another set of charts) we have outlined the prehistoric watershed and valley routes of the great game animals. Our next set of charts showing county development relates itself to the early history of man in the county. These may well be predicated by a general soil map of the county. This can best be developed by using a duplicate topographical map and superimposing upon it information to be had from any state department of agriculture, agricultural college, or from the United States Department of Agriculture at Washington. Such a map will have to presuppose the passing of forests shown on previous maps and must be, therefore—to use a significant newspaper term—a "flash" as to coming events. It is not difficult to secure from the sources mentioned data for a soil map. Experience will prove the wisdom of incorporating on this map the sites of important springs, swamps, and sloughs. This map will serve as a key map as further work of the same sort is undertaken.

By following this program the investigator is now ready to lay the basis for a modern map of the county under survey. This will be a large map based upon the original surveys of each township in the county. These original surveys were deposited in the General Land Office at Washington, and copies can be secured by seeking the assistance of employees of the United States Geological Survey who in odd hours can do the work with scientific accuracy. One complete set of duplicates of these original surveys of every township in your state was deposited by the government at your state capital. These may be found in one of many places; they may be in the State Surveyor's office, in the State Highway Department, or in the Federal Building or office. Here they can always be consulted and copies of them can be made.

These original township surveys form, of themselves, a very interesting study. Made at an early date, they afford much information which may be vainly sought for elsewhere. They usually show the roads and ancient trails, springs, and other local points of importance, old camp sites, etc., known today only in story and legend. Particularly in the West, irrigation projects and other improvements have obliterated many of these places.

When tracings of these survey maps are secured, you have, on a large scale, your future field of work. Only slightly, if at all, do these township surveys show elevations. Using your key maps now in hand, elevations must be drawn in. This should be done by an expert, but the novice will find a pleasure in assisting in the work. Where United States Geological Survey topographical sheets exist this work will be greatly facilitated. If the tracings of the original township are made on linen, different sets of blueprints of them can be struck off for the use of different persons or groups interested; all points on them can be located by the various sections and quarter sections, and boy and girl scouts can be interested in the work of identifying them; many such may be marked temporarily or permanently, according to their importance and the means at the worker's command. They will be inherently interested in following out the routes of any well-known trail and marking, perhaps by flags, its salient positions.

In all such efforts to recreate the past geographically in a scientific way, a large amount of information usually awaits the student in the diaries and journals of old-time travelers. The demand for such information should be met by organizations which have means at their disposal—and when the public realizes the concrete value of the work to be done an unsuspected interest, and monetary support, can be rallied to carry on such projects. From any State Library or State Historical Society[1] information can be had as to the existing journals or diaries of early travelers in your county. In many cases at trifling expense the loan of these documents from a State Library to a local library can be arranged for the use of local investigators. Some may be purchased from old or rare book dealers. In any case, no matter how rare or priceless the original may be, photostat copies can be had at a cost rarely exceeding fifty dollars a volume from any great library where such work is constantly done. At no greater expense the original manuscript diaries or journals may be photostated for the use of students. Information concerning all such details can be had from any large local library, State Library or State Historical Society. There might be found groups of six or eight well-to-do citizens who would be willing to underwrite the expense of photostating one rare book or manuscript journal each, provided that, when it has been used by local investigators, it shall become a part of their private libraries.

It is hardly too much to say that genuine interest in local history in this country would be aroused to a degree never dreamed of if a set of blueprints of copies of the original surveys of any county's townships should be mounted for display in any central public place in each township. An untold amount of valuable information may be secured from "old-timers" when once they are able to see concretely before them the ground plan of their "country." In innumerable instances the present writer has profited thus in every

[1] A type of coöperation afforded by State Historical Societies and State Departments of History is illustrated by this quotation from *Museum Echoes,* of March 1, 1928, issued by the Ohio State Archaeological and Historical Society:

Can your County boast of a County Historical Society? If it does not why not organize one? Every county in the State should possess an active organization of this kind. Every single county has a wealth of historical resources within its confines, over which such an organization should act as guardian. This Society will be pleased to assist any county in organizing such a society and will furnish upon request and free of charge any service, advice, and cooperation possible. Many more Historical Societies in Ohio are deemed essential and will be welcomed.

Cf. articles by Joseph Schafer and T. C. Blegen in Minn. Hist. Soc. *Collections,* IV, 3–20; *Minn. History,* II, No. 1, 11–24.

western state which was traversed by the Oregon, Santa Fé, California, or Mormon trails.[2] It would be well worth the effort for any State Historical Society to offer prizes for the best maps made of any county along these lines—for even such organizations find it difficult to interest the people at large in the specific historical work which they are legally empowered to promote. Many of these would make an excellent use of funds by supplying the sets of blueprints above described.

The bewildering ramifications of our study are patent. If on such maps, bearing the date of the original survey, the data of our previously described key maps is superimposed, the progress of development, of civilization, remains to be laid in. This must be done on different sets of blueprints each bearing the date of successive decades or generations. The development of farms, ranches, or plantations can be noted. Prospective surveys for railways which were or were not built can be shown. The projects for the opening of the county's resources will follow. Towns in the process of development can be charted in their successive stages, showing the background and reasons which existed for their appearance and later decay or expansion. The accounts of first travelers may be studied for the sites of "improvements," early taverns, camping sites; spots famous for sterility or fertility may be platted; perhaps the various stages of a thoroughfare's growth from trail to pavement can be shown with different alignments of courses in different periods of development. Changing courses of drainage systems may be depicted—the disappearance of this stream, that bog or slough. When did the "Black Pool" of the Little Blue in Jefferson County, Nebraska, fade out? Such famous landmarks have a modern history, just as they had a geological background. This may be found in early travelers' descriptions and in later town records or the memory of old residents—as in the interesting case of the Ice Slough previously mentioned. It is impossible to suggest the manifold lines which investigation may take to show soil development, drifts of population, formation of school districts (sometimes these keep alive old place names of significance), rise and passing of religious centers (rural churches), and the kaleidoscopic alterations of political lines and "fences."

2 *Crown Collection of American Maps,* Series IV.

Index

Articles and books mentioned in the foregoing pages are included in this Index under authors' names, forming a working bibliography to date for a subject on which no such aid now exists. The lists of publications of the United States Department of Agriculture, and all State Departments of Agriculture, will also supply vast information on the theme.